Vessel Voyage Data Analysis

Vessel Voyage Data Analysis

A Comparative Study

By

KIM J. LOROCH

CORNELL MARITIME PRESS, INC.

Cambridge   Maryland

1966

Library of Congress Catalog Card Number: 65-20766
Manufactured in the United States of America

Contents

List of Exhibits

Preface

The purpose of this study, which grew out of a Master's thesis accepted by the City College of New York in the spring of 1964, is not to analyze the past or take a mental flight into the future of the shipping world. It strives, in a rather simple way, to organize the flow, presentation, analysis, and interpretation of the mass of vessel operating-data that is or should be made available to those who operate the vessels, build them, and engage in research concerning them, and to those various maritime agencies on governmental and intergovernmental levels. New concepts and approaches within the field of transportation, plus the rising relative importance of transportation in business logistics, provide the specific *raisons d'être* for this volume.

A prominent steamship executive was recently overheard wistfully remarking to his luncheon companions that he was far from satisfied with the way his operating unit treated voyage performances and results. It would seem that he was speaking for a good many ocean-shipping companies the world over. In spite of some attempts and exhortations, this vital two-way link between sea and shore operations remains obscure and neglected. There exist as many systems for dealing with voyage data as there are steamship companies, ranging from extremely elaborate and often computerized methods to the simple filing away and forgetting of the engine and deck logbooks.

The comparative vessel-performance-analysis model described in these pages attempts to set up a uniform system of standardized forms that can be used to guide, record, and measure the accomplishments of ocean-going vessels. Better organization leads to better control, which in turn results in greater efficiency and better utilization of equipment.

Lack of published sources forced the writer to turn to the mail-questionnaire technique for guidance and suggestions. The survey was designed to reach a representative cross-section of the shipping industry throughout the world. The response to this survey indicated a most unsatisfactory situation in the field of vessel-voyage-data analysis. There were a significant number of exceptions to this rule, and the generous cooperation of the individuals and organizations making up these exceptions has helped make this inquiry possible.

If this study helps in some measure to bring into focus the need and the potential of a flexible but universal system of vessel-voyage-data presentation, it will have accomplished its purpose. The writer's ambition will be fulfilled in having brought forth a useful tool which stimulates others to look closer and deeper into the problems it raises and solutions it offers.

The list of people to whom I am indebted for encouragement and assistance is, indeed, a long one. I am grateful to all of them for helping to give this book whatever interest and success it may have.

Kim J. Loroch

Vessel Voyage Data Analysis

CHAPTER I

Introduction

This study attempts, first, to survey and outline the current thinking on the subject of vessel-voyage-data analysis. Next, it suggests, by means of practical examples, a uniform way to collect, process, analyze, and present vessel-voyage data. Finally, it sets forth the economic and practical implications of the suggested comparative method of analysis at the background of profound new developments and trends discernible in the fascinating world of transportation.

RESTRICTED METHODS OF VOYAGE DATA ANALYSIS

The analysis of vessel-service-performance data is receiving a good deal of attention in certain quarters. As the bibliography discloses, several studies on applications of statistical methods to vessel-performance data have been published. Trial and service performances of various selected vessels have been recorded, analyzed, and made available in various technical publications. These discourses, however, are directed at the scientist, naval architect, marine engineer, and shipbuilder. The shipowner, the operator, or the man in the office may not even be aware these papers exist; moreover, he would probably find most of the sophisticated engineering, mathematical, and statistical concepts beyond his grasp. Yet these papers are well interspersed with many everyday operating problems and deserve a wider audience. This gap needs to be bridged, and it is hoped that this study will provide some of the necessary stimulus and possibly a common denominator for doing so.

EVOLUTION OF VOYAGE DATA ANALYSIS

In the days of the coal-burning steamer it was impossible to figure out fuel consumption during short periods. Indicator cards were taken only to check the proper working of the engine's steam and exhaust control mechanism. Log readings were useful to make a guess of the ship's position after a period of steaming during the night or in the fog. It was quite unnecessary to record propeller revolutions in tenths. Nevertheless, the old sea-going engineer was interested in apparent slip of the propeller (and thus in propeller revolutions per minute and vessel speed) because it reflected the external conditions—weather and bottom fouling—under which the vessel was sailing.

Today, accurate and reliable recording of fuel consumption and propeller revolutions per minute does not present a great problem. Vessel logs and torsionmeters are being constantly improved, and propelling-power measurements can be checked with the simultaneous records of fuel consumption, exhaust-gas temperatures, and reports on the main engine's shop trials. It is now possible to ascertain, during the first months of a vessel's life, her standard performance.

Technical and nautical records are collected on board every vessel at sea. In the past, these records were neither complete nor systematic; nobody knew why they were collected in the first place. Nowadays, it is possible to obtain a wealth of reasonably reliable and accurate information about the performance of each individual ship under service conditions.

VESSEL LOGBOOKS

All vessels maintain logbooks, which have been in use for centuries. These familiar documents make up a complete, day-to-day nautical and technical record of the voyage, a record pregnant with operating data. A direct or indirect link can invariably be traced between these basic documents and any report or summary of operations used by a steamship company.

On the subject of logbooks we can do no better than quote what Admiral Edward C. Holden, Jr., said in an article, entitled "Laws a Master Must Know," that appeared some years ago in the *Marine News* (now *World Ports and Marine News*):

One of the most hallowed institutions on board ship is the "Ship's Log," commonly called the "Deck Log." This factual diary of a ship's life and the lives of those on board her is required by law to be kept and supervised by the Master. All entries must be signed by him and by the Mate or some other member of the crew. All entries are required to be made promptly.

A second log called the "Engine Log" is kept by the Chief Engineer. This log contains vital data concerning operations in the engine department.

A third log, called the "Official Log," is required to be kept by the Master in accordance with strict statutory regulations which are printed in the logbook. It must be turned over to the Shipping Commissioner at the end of each voyage for action in regard to fines, disciplinary action and other data according to directions contained therein.

These logs can be a great asset to an owner if properly kept and a great liability if not properly kept. They carry great weight in Coast Guard hearings and in courts of law, not only because of the entries they contain but often because of their omissions.

As any seaman knows, no erasures or alterations are permitted in logbooks. If any change is made, it should be by separate entry, leaving the original entry so that it will be readable; otherwise, the subject matter may be ruled null and void by the courts. (It is much better to write out a proposed log entry in the rough, smooth it out in proper form and then write the entry rather than make errors and serious omissions.)

In addition to the statistical entries in the Deck Log covering such items as state of the wind, sea temperature, barometer, speed, course, engine readings, navigational position, etc., the law requires entries of all such matters as the legal conviction and punishment of members of the crew; offenses charged against and replies of members of the crew; offenses charged and punishments inflicted on board; etc. More than once, a Master who has testified before the Coast Guard in court relative to a case in dispute, under inquiry or in litigation, has been confronted by the opposing counsel with the fact that no proper log entry was made in regard to the case.

It is inevitable that there must be duplication of entries especially in the Deck Log and Official Log. Remember that the Deck Log is a permanent Ship's Log; whereas, the Official Log must be surrendered at the end of each voyage to the Shipping Commissioner. Therefore, it is necessary to include vital entries from the Official Log in the Ship's Log (Deck Log).

Strange as it may seem, it is very difficult to get some Masters and officers to write and maintain a proper logbook—Deck, Engine or Official—often to the detriment of their own interests and that of the shipowner.

The writer, who examined and analyzed many logbooks, is also convinced that those in charge of vessels are not properly impressed with the logbook's importance. One wonders to what extent the maritime training centers are aware of this shortcoming in their product.

United States laws also require log entries of every illness or injury to members of the crew, and their medical treatment; each case of death with the cause thereof; each birth with sex and names of parents; each marriage, with names of the parties; separation of each member of crew from the ship's articles, with time, place, manner and cause thereof; wages for each deceased member of the

crew as due at time of death; proceeds of sale of effects of deceased
crew members; full account of fires, collisions and other casualties;
and entry of ship's draft and position of the loadline at commence-
ment of each voyage. These are the legal requirements for log
entries, but all events which happen on board that are of actual or
potential importance should be logged. Careful thought should be
given such entries so as to make them as brief as possible yet insure
that they are factually complete. If in doubt as to whether or not
an item merits log entry, log it. This is particularly true of minor
illnesses and injuries which only too frequently form the basis of
subsequent claims.

So that the large mass of data contained in the deck and engine
logbooks can be of use to the various departments ashore, it is summarized in "abstract logs," which extract for office use the required
key information from the vessel logbooks.

RELIABILITY OF LOGBOOK DATA

There have been wide differences of opinion as to the reliability
and accuracy of the logbooks and their abstracts. Some have stated
that voyage data as recorded in the logbooks by the ship's personnel
is unreliable and inconsistent and that analysis is not worthwhile.
Wind, weather, sea conditions; slowing down for policy reasons or
to meet certain critical arrivals; machinery defects and break-
downs; inefficient operation of the vessel's propulsion machinery;
defective instrumentation; and the human error in recording the
essential data, all make an accurate and detailed analysis of the
vessel's performance in service difficult. In the case of the engineer's logbook, data is sometimes biased because of the engineer's
inclination to show that he has developed a very considerable horsepower, which brings the consumption of fuel per horsepower per
hour down and apparent efficiency up.

On the other hand, there are some who find the logbook voyage
data neither unreliable nor inconsistent; the entries are no doubt
subject to personal errors but the record, they point out, is made
in good faith. Logbooks and abstracts, from the scientific point of
view, may not be perfect. But if he is really interested in his vessels'
performance, the shipowner has no choice but to study the vast
mass of information contained in them, since they constitute his
principal source of information. The same applies for the naval
architect, who should follow the ship after it has left the shipyard,
pursue its history, and draw from the results of the vessel's service
her average speed, amount of fuel and lubricating-oil consumption,
and many other factors that will guide him in designing future

vessels. The analysis itself should be executed by qualified members of the shore staff. In this way the benefits of the analysis are immediately and directly at the disposal of the owner, who comes to know his ships individually and who can make decisions that will mean profits in operation.

REVIVAL OF INTEREST IN VOYAGE DATA

Material published on service performance of vessels is very limited. This is regrettable from the viewpoints of both the shipbuilder and the shipowner. The former usually loses sight of his product the day the ship is commissioned, and in most cases gains little or nothing from the owner's experience after the ship is in service. An exchange of information between the builder and the owner in performance investigations is mutually beneficial. The shipowner is vitally concerned in obtaining, among other things, as high an average speed as possible for a minimum amount of fuel consumption. Because of insufficient service-performance data, the shipbuilder is prevented from achieving a higher average service speed for a given shaft horsepower output.

Differences in output between similar ships mean either that the efficiencies were different when the ships were new, one ship deteriorated in service more than another, or that one ship may be operated less efficiently by her crew. Assuming that both vessels entered service equally efficient, it is obvious that the proper analysis of service performance could make or break a successful operation.

It is no wonder, therefore, that there has recently been a revival of interest in voyage performances and results. Evidence of this trend was contained in the responses to the survey analyzed in the next chapter. The interest has been brought on partly by the fact that the accumulation and manipulation of data, formerly almost prohibitively expensive, can today be handled rapidly and efficiently at an astonishingly economical rate by electronic means.

Moreover, ocean shipping along with other modes of transportation is going through a stage of significant changes and developments which are elevating vessel-performance analysis to a greater importance in the overall picture. The final chapter takes a brief look at these new developments.

THE SCIENTIST VIS-Á-VIS THE SHIPOWNER

The naval architect, shipbuilder, and shipowner are all vitally interested in vessel-service performance. A new ship must meet specified requirements during acceptance trials, but this is small comfort to the shipowner if after entry into service there is an appreciable deterioration in performance. To the designers and builders, voyage data means certain specific performances, while the shipowner is mainly interested in a quantitative comparison between sea-going qualities of different vessels.

The scientist, then, looks not only for a high degree of accuracy in vessel-service data, but also information of wider scope than the shipowner needs. To fulfill his demand would necessitate the installation of more costly though more accurate and reliable recording instruments on individual vessels, knowledge of such instrumentation, and handling experience. The expenditure on additional trained manpower, both afloat and ashore, and the cost of the necessary equipment would be high and scarcely justifiable.

Since sea-going personnel are without the necessary scientific qualifications, specialized training may be the answer to the problem. There is no doubt that the deck officer and the engineer of today are superior in technical and general educational training to their counterparts of, say, twenty years ago. Their training and knowledge continue to grow with the introduction of more sophisticated aids to navigation and shiphandling. When, for example, radar came into the picture as standard equipment, it became necessary to institute radar courses and train competent radar operators. Special training in scientific recording of voyage data given on a selective basis to sea-going personnel would call for a minimum of investment. This special training might be rewarded by a small bonus; selectivity and the consequent prestige, however, might have sufficient appeal to prospective candidates. Of course, there remains the problem of supplying the vessels with the required specialized instrumentation for recording voyage data. Some kind of a lease arrangement appears feasible for such a scheme which could bring the scientist and the shipowner much closer together, with one or two of the various professional and trade associations acting as liaison.

It has recently been disclosed that the American Mail Line and the United States Navy have worked out an experimental venture to see if private shipping can help in the government's growing program to explore the oceans. The pilot test calls for one of the AML's vessels to take on board two scientists and a portable laboratory fitted with various equipment for the collection of oceanographic data. This cooperative effort, although received with mixed emotions by the shipping industry, might serve as a model and guide toward a scientific solution to the problem of collecting vessel-service-performance data.

While automation and the introduction of related sophisticated recording instruments and performance data-loggers, may solve the scientist's problems as regards certain specific vessel-performance data he requires, this is not true of the ship operator. The ship operator needs bases for his accounting system and the economic decisions he must make; logbook data properly collected, analyzed, and presented is still his best bet.

SUMMARY AND CONCLUSIONS

This introductory chapter has surveyed the evolution and progress of vessel-voyage-data analysis as seen by those who build the vessels and those who operate them. Although all segments of the shipping industry can derive benefits from an orderly and possibly standardized approach to collection and analysis of vessel-voyage data, it is the shipowner and his operating man who occupy the spotlight in this study.

It is agreed that systematic collection of vessel-performance records should become a tradition; the records should be complete and compiled conscientiously. The human element and varying qualities of ship and machinery might account for appreciable differences in voyage-data records over a limited period. Comparison over a long period should not be affected. Results consistently recorded and analyzed should become the criteria of ship performance. If there is a guiding thought that the author wishes to convey, it is that there should be consistent recording and analyzing of voyage data as a standard matter of practice for any vessel operator worth his salt.

Chapter II

Voyage Data Survey Response

The survey already referred to was conducted by means of the mail-questionnaire technique. The letter and the questionnaire (reproduced in Appendix A) were sent to a representative cross-section of the world shipping industry. The survey drew returns from 63 out of the 154 selected organizations, equivalent to a 40.4 per cent response, which is generally considered to be a reliable sample.

Although the questions were designed primarily for vessel operating-companies, various maritime institutions were invited to comment and offer suggestions. Of the latter, only a few replied, with a typical answer being:

In response . . . we are sorry to inform you that we will not be able to complete the form as we do not own or operate any vessels.

An ironic twist was supplied by many responding steamship companies who suggested these very associations and institutions as the best contacts for help and guidance.

The response, which took the form of completed questionnaires as well as separate letters, ranged from a simple expression of acknowledgment, interest, and encouragement to the most generous description of what is being done and should be done by the industry in the field of vessel-voyage-data analysis.

Locus of Responsibility

Sifting the replies to determine what department within a company is responsible for collecting, analyzing, and presenting vessel-voyage data resulted in the tabular presentation on the next page.

It was startling to find 24 different companies with 15 different views and approaches. However, the diversity is probably more apparent than real, since, for a variety of reasons, different companies are likely to employ different terminology for similar functions. Nevertheless, it would seem that a clear functional description would go a long way towards eliminating confusion. Moreover, it is quite evident that in the majority of cases, the job of collecting and analyzing vessel-voyage data is a subservient and neglected function hidden among many others which take precedence. If the true value of properly gathered and analyzed voyage data was understood, there would be an independent department closely allied with the operating division. Alternatively, a clearly-identified section attached to or within an operating department might be able to do the job quite adequately.

TABLE 1

LIST OF VARIOUS DEPARTMENTS RESPONSIBLE FOR
VESSEL VOYAGE DATA

Name	Number
1. Marine Department	5
2. Operating Department	3
3. Operating and Statistical Departments	2
4. Marine Technical and Statistical Departments	2
5. Marine Department and Controller's Office	2
6. Scheduling and Performance Department	1
7. Marine Superintendent	1
8. Marine Traffic Department	1
9. Records Department	1
10. Traffic Department	1
11. Accounting Department	1
12. Application and Development Division	1
13. Steamship Statistics	1
14. Operating Department—Performance Analysis Section	1
15. Several Departments (shared responsibility)	1
Total	24

LOGBOOKS AND ABSTRACTS

Deck and engine log abstracts (sometimes called steaming or operating summaries), port logs, canal transit logs, and lay-up logs comprise the basic forms in use for extracting the voyage operating essentials and highlights from the vessel's logbooks. The logbooks themselves, as a rule, are not available to the office personnel until an appreciable time after a voyage is completed.

It has been suggested that in the maintenance of the vessel's logbooks too much emphasis is being placed on matters that are the particular concern of the individual company's policy with regard to types of ships operated and the kinds of goods and commodities carried. This and the always conservative attitude of the industry appear to be the only major obstacles to the standardization of logbooks. Although our main concern here is to champion a cause for the standardization of the abstract logs and voyage-performance statements, standardization of the logbooks themselves undoubtedly deserves probing; it appears both feasible and desirable. Such a project could perhaps be embraced by the many studies initiated by the United States Maritime Administration. Some of these studies are considering the economics and feasibility of a uniform comparative analysis of vessel-voyage data. Why not consider a standardized design for deck and engine logbooks at the same time? Why not go still further and explore the possibility for worldwide standardized logbooks? This could be placed on an intergovernmental plane by requesting IMCO, the United Nations' maritime agency, to investigate its possibilities. One can foresee many difficulties and obstacles to such a proposal, but with English being the language of the sea and the seafarer, are they insurmountable?

DISPATCH AND RECEIPT OF VOYAGE DATA

The following cumulative tabular presentation relates the number of companies to the time elapsed between the end of a voyage and the receipt of the key data necessary for a complete analysis of the voyage.

TABLE 2

CUMULATIVE NUMBER OF FIRMS AND ELAPSING TIME RANGES
BETWEEN END OF VOYAGE AND RECEIPT OF DOCUMENTS

Time Range	Number of Firms
1 day or less	1
1 — 3 days	4
1 — 7 days	10
1 — 15 days	18
1 — 30 days	23
1 — 60 days	25
1 — 90 days	26

The range of time, extending from 24 hours to three months, appears to be directly related to the system of analysis employed. The more meaningful the method and the more important its role within the organization, the less time it takes for the raw data to reach the office. Voyage results that are more than seven days old may be compared to yesterday's newspapers.

SYSTEMS OF ANALYSIS IN USE

The survey confirmed that vessel sea and port performances are scrutinized and certain conclusions are drawn and acted upon, but when it comes to outlining the system employed, one might just as well be asking for classified information. Scant reference was made by some respondents to time, speed, fuel consumption, revolutions and slip of the propeller, as criteria used by voyage analysts. The cost aspect was repeated ad nauseam, creating an impression that voyage-data collection and presentation are done solely for the benefit of the accounting department. This observation is not intended to minimize the important place of costs in operations. Nevertheless, this approach is a limited one and needs to be corrected.

Several specialized transportation companies, to be sure, had no qualms about describing their own thorough sea and port vessel-performance-analysis systems. Incidentally, these few companies have not only built a properly-named department around their voyage analysts, but have also widened its horizons. It comes as no surprise to find these companies also in the forefront of automation and scientific control of steamship operations generally. Furthermore, these same companies are the recognized leaders in the shipping industry in terms of efficiency and profitability.

COMPARATIVE FEATURES

Vessels operating in a given trade can be compared at regular intervals on a same-ship-voyage-to-voyage basis, or with sister-ship operation, on a fleet basis. The majority of operators who analyze completed voyages have introduced some comparative features into their systems. One tramp operator contended that comparison is of no value when conditions change all the time and remain beyond control. One can argue, with some measure of success, that somewhere along the line even tramps are bound to repeat previous voyages or come so close to them that a record for comparative purposes may be useful.

Averages and percentages, the familiar and popular measures of differences, represent the basic tools in any comparative method. Both of them were mentioned frequently and so were tables and graphs. Appendix G carries some notes on the use and application of graphs, diagrams, and visual control boards.

PERFORMANCE STANDARDS AND RATINGS

Most of the performance standards in use appear to be based on model-basin tests and trial trips modified by subsequent actual experience. Charter party guarantees, financial experience, cargo-handling equipment specifications, and the forces of supply and demand for tonnage were also mentioned as yielding standard-performance data. Whether the standards are being compared with actual performance in such a way that a rating or ranking (most likely expressed as percentage) is established, could not be determined. Nobody will quarrel with a well-conceived system for rating performances, but, although desirable, it is not an easy thing to establish. It is doubtful whether a consistent, fair, and foolproof rating method that can be satisfactorily applied to voyage results has been formulated by any steamship company.

UTILIZATION OF VOYAGE PERFORMANCE STATEMENTS

The consensus is that everybody who is anybody within an organization should have access to vessel-performance statements, except, for some reason, the master and the chief engineer. Although no two replies agreed in the list of departments utilizing the statements, almost every possible department within an organization was mentioned.

A system that does not provide the master and the chief engineer with a chance to study the evaluation and comparison reveals a serious shortcoming. The absence of any specific or even indirect references to such practice leads one to conclude that the people who supply the raw data and alone can vouch for its authenticity, are often inadvertently left out of the picture.

NEED FOR A STANDARDIZED SYSTEM

Various reservations expressed by a number of respondents point to a distinct awareness that standardization of voyage-data collection and analysis faces real complications, but that it is nevertheless desirable.

The proposal for a standardized approach and method received a strong expression of support in the questionnaire returned by the Canadian Dominion Bureau of Statistics. The Water Transport Unit of the Bureau enthusiastically views the possibility of basing its work on a uniform comparative analysis adopted by the shipping industry instead of applying its own inherently difficult method of analyzing vessel-voyage data. The measurement of the water transportation function which enters into Canada's foreign trade, national accounts, and balance of payments, could undergo considerable expansion and refinement. Undoubtedly, adoption of a standardized method and appropriate forms by the shipping industry would create national and even international implications with, for the most part, desirable end-results for all who are concerned with maritime matters.

On the other hand, a spokesman for the Military Sea Transportation Service (Atlantic Area) stated in response to the survey questionnaire that a universal standardized system is not possible or needed by them or the shipping industry. A definitive statement of this kind calls for some elaboration, to say the least, but none was supplied. This statement reflects rather strongly the insulated existence that characterizes MSTS: no competition, no need for operating efficiency, and therefore no interest in the tools for measuring its performance.

An acceptable universal method for analyzing voyage data was also enthusiastically endorsed by two of our maritime training centers, suggesting they would be interested in making it part of their curriculum.

SUGGESTIONS AND OTHER COMMENTS

Most respondents agreed that the proposed investigation into voyage-data collection and analysis might be of great potential benefit to the maritime industry. Valuable suggestions and words of encouragement came from people whose names are well known on the American and world scenes: Edward V. Lewis, Harry Benford, Victor A. Lewinson, and Robert H. Langner, to mention only a few.

Mr. Lewinson of Arthur D. Little, Inc., writes that:[1]

Our maritime studies for the Maritime Administration and other clients have emphasized the value of logs as a source of data, and we know how varied the logs and their abstracts are. It would be helpful to have some standard form for analyzing logs.

The questionnaire was designed to invite wishful thinking and a bit of daydreaming. Regretfully, it must be said that the few comments and suggestions that were offered reveal simply that the operating people in the shipping industry have little use or time for such an endeavor. The constructive thoughts, not surprisingly, could easily be related and traced to well-constructed performance

---

[1] Letter from Victor A. Lewinson, Arthur D. Little, Inc., November 6, 1963, Cambridge, Massachusetts.

analysis already in use or in the process of being developed. The shortcomings that were pointed out centered about not having the vessel-service data made available to the management in a more useful and meaningful form. The need for more standards, a more complete analysis of voyage results, and a better comparison of the results made up the extent of the suggestions.

Container operations as practiced by Sea-Land Service, Inc., are relatively new to ocean transportation. This prominent company argues, with some measure of success, that its[2] "specialized cargo handling system has created a requirement for some very specialized forms which are not adaptable generally on an industry-wide basis." Upon reflection, however, is this not equally true of all the traditional operations? The passenger, liner, or tanker trades each uses its own unadaptable forms and rightly so. Clearly, such forms must remain outside the focus of this study.

Perhaps the most gratifying aspect of the survey conducted by the writer was the number of requests for the opportunity to examine the outcome of the investigation. The Department of the Navy, for example, although unable to extend any help because naval voyage data is classified information, felt that some aspects of this study may contribute to improving its practices for naval ships.[3] It is hoped that the publication of this study will sustain and add to the interest in vessel-voyage-data analysis that the survey seemed to have awakened.

VESSEL VOYAGE DATA AND COMPUTERS

The entry of computers into the world of business means that the complexity of vessel-voyage-data collection and analysis can now be detached from the lengthy and costly human effort involved. The shipping industry, at least the progressive and prosperous segments of it, is seriously considering and experimenting with handling and manipulating voyage data at electronic speeds with the help of computers.

One of the many advances in marine engineering in the past decade has been the introduction of data-logging to engine-room installations. The conventional hand-written record is gradually disappearing from vessel engine rooms. Some of the latest marine data-logging systems are able to provide at regular intervals an

---

[2] Letter from C. R. Cushing, Sea-Land Service, Inc., January 21, 1964, Elizabeth, New Jersey.

[3] Letter from N. Sonenshein, Captain, USN, Director of Ship Design, Bureau of Ships, Department of the Navy, December 9, 1963, Washington, D.C.

automatically written routine engineering log. A new-type data-logger system of monitoring machinery efficiency, called the K Logger, has been recently unveiled by the Socony Mobil Oil Company. It differs from other normal data-logging systems in that it plots variations and charts them for immediate perusal.

Shell International Marine of London was good enough to supply an article, which, because of its importance and bearing, is quoted in its entirety as it was written for the British periodical *New Scientist* (No. 375: January 23, 1964, p. 215) by R. M. Duggan of Shell International under the title "An Experiment in Ship-to-Shore Telemetry."

We are now midway through a two-year experiment at Shell International Marine aimed at detecting and pinpointing changes in the performance of our tankers at sea. The signs are that the system we are evolving will be of immense value to the company in improving efficiency, and eventually to shipowners generally.

What Shell is developing is a telemetry system for recording data on board ship, anywhere in the world, transmitting this information by radio and land-line to London, and analyzing it at the Shell Centre.

A vessel's performance deteriorates from the moment she embarks on her trials. A year's service may see a substantial reduction in her performance owing to hull and propeller problems, such as damage, fouling and corrosion, and engine deterioration. Performance data are recorded in the ship's log, of course, although these are limited and of little practical purpose; in any case the data are analyzed, if at all, only when the logbooks can be returned to head office, which may be months later. Yet another drawback has been pointed up rather dramatically by Shell's investigations over the past two years, namely, that ship-board instruments are notoriously unreliable.

The only sure means for assessing the deterioration in performance available at present is to take the ship out of service and put it through trials over an accurately measured mile—an expensive and time-consuming process. Moreover, for large tankers there is a further problem in that there are only two "trial grounds" available, off Malta and off Scotland.

We are developing a system that will transmit the data needed to make a full statistical analysis of a ship's performance throughout the time she is at sea, and will do so rapidly and accurately. The first step, naturally, was to relate the observations to the established "measured-mile" technique, and this we did with the tanker *Sitala* (79,500 tons deadweight) in trials off Malta. The comparison was very encouraging, and we went ahead with the development of more reliable means of gathering and transmitting data.

A little later, in experiments with the tanker *Hemifusus*, the Shell investigators had the satisfaction of spotting a sudden deterioration

in propeller efficiency, caused by damage which, owing to the changing circumstances of the vessel's activities at the time, had passed
unnoticed.

A year ago the application and development department of Shell
International Marine adopted the idea and began a two-year experiment involving 15 tankers; these are of three basic sizes (large,
medium and small) and sail under flags of several nations. Three
of the tankers are now equipped with automatic means for logging
data manually, taking readings every four-hour watch. The information recorded includes three identification numbers, nine temperatures, speed, revolutions, power thrust, various weather conditions,
fore and aft draught, rudder angle, boiler pressure, fuel density,
and the flow and pressure of steam.

It was not enough simply to record data accurately, however, and
there was still the need to relay it back to the computer in London,
quickly and without introducing errors. A few months ago, Shell
settled for the Autospec system of data transmission, with its facil-
ity for detecting and correcting errors and for transmitting over
considerable distances. In its latest form, using two sets of aerials
and single-side-band transmission, we can form a data link with
vessels as far away as Singapore; with double-side-band transmission we can still get excellent results as far as Aden.

For the past six months we have had this system operating in
the tanker *Serenia*. She sends a tape to the Shell Centre each day
and any suspected errors are checked with her within 24 hours,
while there is a good chance of the data still being available. Information collected by her data-collection system is transferred to
punched tape, which provides the signal that is sent out by her radio
transmitter on the wide-band channel. The signal is picked up by
the Post Office at Bearley, Staffordshire, and re-routed through
land-lines to the Shell Centre, where an IBM computer is being
used to make statistical analyses of performance.

Meanwhile, nine other tankers (it will be twelve next month) are
gathering data by hand, recording it on tape and posting it to
London; in these cases there is a delay of a month or so.

By the end of the second year of the Shell experiment we hope to
be able to show that these telemetering techniques can replace the
time-consuming and troublesome "measured-mile" method of assessing performance. If we are successful, one of the first direct results
of having up-to-the-minute reports on the state of a vessel should
be their use in planning dockings. Again, damage to the propeller
is a surprisingly frequent reason for impaired efficiency, and its
prompt detection would be a considerable advantage. From the
research and development point of view there will be a "payoff" in
terms of information on corrosion and hull fouling, leading perhaps
to new hull-coating treatment.

Moreover, it is hoped that a direct contribution can be made to
studies on the hydrodynamics of ships. The ship division of the
National Physical Laboratory, and the British Ship Research Association, both of which have assisted the investigations—the
former especially by helping with the formulation of terms used

in our equation for statistical analysis—should receive a feedback
in the form of confirmation of empirical laws they have derived
from model testing.

Shell International appears to have taken the engine-room automatic data-logging system one step further by having the data
quickly relayed by radio to its London computer for immediate
analysis. The system sounds excellent for what it does and as far
as it goes, but is not comprehensive enough from the ship operator's
point of view. It relies on data gathered while the ship is under
way, data almost wholly related to engine performance. For this
reason it is rather difficult to accept this method, if it can be called
that, as one capable of doing the whole job of collecting, analyzing,
and presenting voyage data as it is understood in this study.
Although final judgment and evaluation must be deferred until
the Shell people publish their final report, the method described in
these pages is not likely to clash, supersede, or be superseded by
other systems, such as Shell's. On the contrary, any other method,
unless equally comprehensive, must necessarily be complementary
in character, scope, and application, or capable of improving only
certain aspects of the total approach.

SUMMARY AND CONCLUSIONS

The survey response was, on the whole, most gratifying for what
it revealed and did not reveal. There is no doubt that steamship
operations, shipbuilding, research, governmental and intergovernmental planning and assistance, and all ancillary maritime organizations would benefit from an orderly and uniform presentation and
analysis of vessel-performance data. There is willingness and
readiness among the majority of these interests for adoption of an
acceptable universal method.

Examination of the survey yields the following conclusions and
observations:

1. There is a need for recognizing a clearly-defined and autono-
mous function for the collection and analysis of vessel-voyage data.

2. There is a need to widen, enlarge, and elevate the vessel-
voyage-data analysis function in order to reap full benefits.

3. There is a need to introduce simple and possibly standardized
data-collection forms to bring about an efficient and orderly analysis
of voyage performances.

4. The method and the forms used for data collection should per-
mit those responsible for supplying the information to complete the
forms within hours after the end of the voyage.

5. A good method for analyzing vessel-voyage data should embrace comparative features for better interpretation of individual and overall results.

6. A good use can be made of the many simple and even sophisticated statistical and operations research tools.

7. A well-conceived system of rating vessel performances may be difficult to develop, yet very desirable.

8. The consensus is that everybody who is anybody within an organization should have access to vessel-performance statements including the sea-going executives, that is, the master and the chief engineer.

9. The majority of steamship operating units would consider adoption of an acceptable uniform approach to analyzing vessel-voyage data; standardization may be somewhat complicated yet very desirable. Marine research, naval architecture, maritime education, manufacturers of machinery and components, and many governmental and intergovernmental units would find such a uniform approach helpful in their efforts to expand and refine their work.

10. The lengthy and costly human effort involved in collecting and analyzing complex voyage data has been eliminated by computers. The progressive segments of the shipping industry accept automatic data-processing systems as offering the ultimate in the quest for efficiency and intelligent planning.

11. The subject of vessel-voyage-data analysis, as it is understood in this study, receives surprisingly little attention in the world of ocean shipping; it requires more study in depth.

The maritime industry is far from monolithic. Flexibility and adaptability must of necessity be built into any acceptable standardized method for analyzing vessel performances. Moving goods or people across the waters, which is the only common denominator, has led to specialization dictated by economics and other considerations. Ocean carriage, as any other industry, has been affected by the principle of division of labor and the advantages it offers; certain aspects of ship operation become more or less meaningful depending on what it is one carries. Liner, tramp, passenger, tanker, or bulk carrier operations reveal many logical differences, but these differences do not change or eliminate the basic need for an analysis of vessel-voyage results.

The next chapter will explore and attempt to formulate a uniform comparative method for analyzing vessel-voyage data.

CHAPTER III

The Method

How can the function of analyzing vessel-voyage performances be executed more effectively? Since functions are performed by systems, it is the latter that must be examined and improved. A system links a number of elements in such a way that it assumes a facilitating effect on the carrying-out of a process.

This chapter will examine the elements of the suggested system by looking at a number of forms designed for the collection, analysis, and presentation of the basic vessel-voyage data. The following chapter will go over an example of a step-by-step analysis of a completed voyage to clarify and determine the place and application of the various forms in the system. Both chapters, it is hoped, will provide at least a partial answer to the question: How can the function of analyzing vessel-voyage performances be executed more effectively?

ABSTRACT LOGS: LONG FORM

The deck and engine logbooks, as we have already seen, provide the complete and final source of all basic vessel-operating data. However, the mass of technical and nautical information which finds its way into the logbooks is unwieldy as well as not readily available. Consequently, most operating steamship companies have evolved means to extract the pertinent data for office use. The employment of abstract logs, as these extracts have come to be known, is a popular and familiar method of collecting the required vessel-voyage data.

Complete voyage abstracts, as a rule, consist of the following forms:

      a. Deck Abstract Log (see Exhibit I)
      b. Engine Abstract Log (see Exhibit II)
      c. Voyage Port Log (see Exhibit III)
      d. Canal Transit Log (see Exhibit IV)
      e. Lay-Up Port Log (see Exhibit V)

EXHIBIT I

DECK ABSTRACT LOG

/s._____

VOYAGE NO._____

_____
MASTER

N O T E

THIS ABSTRACT LOG IS TO BE FILLED OUT FOR A
ROUND VOYAGE STARTING AND FINISHING AT THE
HOME PORT. EACH SEPARATE PASSAGE FROM PORT
TO PORT TO BE SHOWN TOTALED AND AVERAGED,
THEN LEAVE ONE LINE BLANK AND CONTINUE ON
SAME PAGE. TO BE HANDED IN ON ARRIVAL AT THE
HOME PORT.

EXHIBIT I

ABSTRACT LOG

DATE AND TIME	POSITION AT NOON		DISTANCE BY D. R.	DISTANCE BY OBSV	DURATION STEAMING DAY		AVERAGE SPEED PER HOUR	COURSE	WIND		SEA	REMARKS
	LATITUDE	LONGITUDE			HRS.	MIN.			DIRECTION	BEAUFORT SCALE		

EXHIBIT I

START AND FINISH OF PASSAGES—DRAFT OF VESSEL

STARTED AT	DATE	A. M.		P. M.		DRAFT						FINISHED AT	DATE	A. M.		P. M.		DRAFT						
		HR.	MIN.	HR.	MIN.	FWD.		AFT.		MEAN				HR.	MIN.	HR.	MIN.	FWD.		AFT.		MEAN	
						FT.	IN.	FT.	IN.	FT.	IN.							FT.	IN.	FT.	IN.	FT.	IN.

RUNNING TIME AND DETENTIONS ON PASSAGES

STARTED AT	FINISHED AT	RUNNING TIME			DIFF. LONG. TIME			ELAPSED TIME			DATE	DETENTION AT	DETENTIONS ON PASSAGES			REMARKS
		D	H	M	D	H	M	D	H	M			D	H	M	
	TOTAL															
PANAMA CANAL ATLANTIC TO PACIFIC																
PANAMA CANAL PACIFIC TO ATLANTIC																
TOTAL OF ALL PASSAGES																

EXHIBIT I

BALLAST REPORT

WATER IN TANKS (TONS OF 2240 LBS.)

NAME OF PORT

TANKS		ARRIVING	LEAVING	ARRIVING	LEAVING	ARRIVING	LEAVING	ARRIVING	LEAVING	ARRIVING	LEAVING
CENTER LINE TANKS	Fore Peak										
	Deep Tanks Forward S										
	Deep Tanks Forward P										
	No. 1										
	No. 2										
	Deep Tank Amidships										
	No. 3										
	No. 4										
	No. 5										
SIDE TANKS	No. 1 P										
	No. 1 S										
	No. 2 P										
	No 2 S										
	No. 3 P										
	No. 3 S										
	No. 4 P										
	No. 4 S										
	No. 5 P										
	No. 5 S										
	No. 6 P										
	No. 6 S										
	No. 7 P										
	No. 7 S										
	No. 8 P										
	No. 8 S										
	No. 9 P										
	No. 9 S										
	Aft Peak										
	TOTAL BALLAST										

EXHIBIT I

CARGO AND DEADWEIGHT IN TONS OF 2240 POUNDS

NAME OF PORT

DESCRIPTION	ARRIVING	LEAVING	ARRIVING	LEAVING	ARRIVING	LEAVING	ARRIVING	LEAVING	ARRIVING	LEAVING
Cargo										
Ballast										
Fuel										
All Fresh Water										
All Stores										
TOTALS										

Remarks regarding cargo and deadweight

FUEL OIL ON BOARD IN BARRELS

NAME OF PORT

TANKS	ARRIVING	LEAVING	ARRIVING	LEAVING	ARRIVING	LEAVING	ARRIVING	LEAVING
No. 1 Forward								
No. 2 Forward								
No. 3 Aft Port								
No. 3 Aft Stbd.								
Settler Port								
Settler Stbd.								
TOTAL FUEL OIL IN BARRELS								
TOTAL FUEL OIL IN TONS OF 2240 LBS.								

EXHIBIT I

CAPTAIN'S FUEL REPORT

REMAINING FROM VOYAGE NO.		BARRELS
FUEL RECEIVED	BARRELS	
At		
At		
At		
At		
TOTAL FUEL RECEIVED		

TOTAL FUEL REMAINING AND RECEIVED

FUEL CONSUMED

PASSAGE	AT SEA BARRELS	IN PORT BARRELS	TOTAL BARRELS
A			
B			
C			
D			
E			
F			
G			
H			
I			
PANAMA CANAL ATLANTIC TO PACIFIC			
PANAMA CANAL PACIFIC TO ATLANTIC			
TOTAL CONSUMED ON VOYAGE			
REMAINING FOR VOYAGE NO.			

NOTE: Fuel oil to be shown in barrels.

DATE AND TIME	

EXHIBIT II

ENGINE ABSTRACT LOG

/s. _____

VOYAGE No._____

_____
CHIEF ENGINEER

N O T E

THIS ABSTRACT LOG IS TO BE FILLED OUT FOR A ROUND VOYAGE STARTING AND FINISHING AT THE HOME PORT. EACH SEPARATE PASSAGE FROM PORT TO PORT TO BE SHOWN TOTALED AND AVERAGED, THEN LEAVE ONE LINE BLANK AND CONTINUE ON SAME PAGE. TO BE HANDED IN ON ARRIVAL AT THE HOME PORT.

EXHIBIT II

ABSTRACT LOG

PAGE 1 — TIME / DISTANCE / PRESSURES / TEMPERATURES

TIME: Hrs., Min. — DISTANCE: Obsv., Eng. — Slip %, Knots obsv., RPM, No. of nozzles, Bbls. fuel per day, Lbs. fuel per SHP/hr., S.H.P. torsion meter reading

PRESSURES: Main steam superheater outlet (Port, Stbd.), Steam of H.P. tur. chest, H.P. bldr. steam, L.P. tur. inlet, L.P. bldr., Vac. m. cond., Gland seal steam

TEMPERATURES: Main superheater outlet (Port, Stbd.), H.P. bldr. chest, H.P. bldr. steam, H.P. bldr.

DATE NOON OF

ABSTRACT LOG

PAGE 2 — TEMPERATURES / PRESSURES / LUBE OIL / BOILER WATER TEST

TEMPERATURES: L.P. bleeder, L.P. exhaust, Main cond. pump disch., 1st stage feed htr. outlet, Deaerator outlet, Economizer outlet (Port, Stbd.)

PRESSURES: Injection temp., Main cond. Disch. temp., Shell press, Main circulator, Cond. pump disch., Aux. cond. Aux. circulator, Main feed pump disch., 1st stage feed htr. shell, Deaerator feed htr. shell, Governor oil

LUBE OIL: Pump no., L.O. heater, Pump disch. press., L.O. cooler inlet temp., L.O. cooler outlet temp.

BOILER WATER TEST: Hardness, Phena. alkalinity, Total alkalinity, Chlorides salinity, Phosphate, Sulphite dissolved oxygen, P.H. of condensate, Flash blow, Long blow

DATE NOON OF

ABSTRACT LOG

PAGE 3 — NUMBER HOURS IN USE / FRESH WATER USED / FUEL OIL

NUMBER HOURS IN USE: Evaporators (Inboard, Outboard), Pump room ballast pumps, Low pressure steam generator, Diesel generator, Lub. oil separator, Oil pressure at header, Temp. of oil at header, Size of tips, Number burners in use (Port, Stbd.), Pump disch. press., Pump no., Fuel oil meter U. S. Gals., RPM counter reading, Wind force, Weather

FRESH WATER USED: Dis-tilled feed tons, Wash water tons, Drink-ing water tons, Temp. F. W. made

FWD, AFT Draft, Temperature, State of Sea

DATE NOON OF

ABSTRACT LOG

PAGE 4 — AIR PRESSURE / AIR & GAS TEMP. / TEMPERATURE OF / LOW PRESSURE STEAM GENERATOR / L. P. EVAPORATOR / MAIN GENERATORS

AIR PRESSURE: Draft at fan discharge (Port, Stbd.), Draft at burners (Port, Stbd.), Furnace pressure (Port, Stbd.), Uptake pressure (Port, Stbd.)

AIR & GAS TEMP. °F: Air from header (Port, Stbd.), Uptake (Port, Stbd.), CO_2 at uptakes (Port, Stbd.)

TEMPERATURE OF: Boiler room, Engine room, Feed Water M. U. S. Gal.

LOW PRESSURE STEAM GENERATOR: STEAM FROM Bleeder, Reducing valve, Steam supply pressure, Generator shell pressure, Feed pump No., Chloride test, Alkalinity, Hardness

L. P. EVAPORATOR: Steam source L. P. bleeder auxy. exhaust, Meter reading

MAIN GENERATORS: AVERAGE Volts, K. W., Gen. in use inboard or outboard

DATE NOON OF

30

EXHIBIT II

SUMMARY OF TOTALS AND AVERAGES ON PASSAGES AND ROUND VOYAGE

PASSAGE	FROM	TO	TIME FULL SPEED			TIME REDUCED SPEED			TIME ENGINE STOPPED			DISTANCES		Slip %	REVOLUTIONS		Knots obsv.	FUEL	FUEL AVERAGE		
			D.	H.	M.	D.	H.	M.	D.	H.	M.	Obsv.	Eng.		Total	Per min.		Total barrels for passage	Barrels per day	Barrels per mile	Engine miles per bbl.
A																					
B																					
C																					
D																					
E																					
F																					
G																					
H																					
		TOTAL																			
Panama Canal Atlantic to Pacific																					
" " Pacific to Atlantic																					
TOTAL OF ALL PASSAGES																					

RUNNING TIME AND DETENTIONS ON PASSAGES

PASSAGE	RUNNING TIME PASSAGE			DIFF. LONG TIME PASSAGE			ELAPSED TIME PASSAGE			DETENTIONS ON PASSAGES								
	D.	H.	M.	D.	H.	M.	D.	H.	M.	Date	Detention at	D.	H.	M.	REMARKS			
A																		
B																		
C																		
D																		
E																		
F																		
G																		
H																		
TOTAL																		
Panama Canal Atlantic to Pacific																		
" " Pacific to Atlantic																		
TOTAL OF ALL PASSAGES																		

ON PASSAGES FOR ALL PURPOSES		DURING DETENTIONS	IN PORT		REMARKS
Passage	Bbls. used	Bbls. used		Bbls. used	Fuel consumed during off hire (repair period, etc.)..........BBLS.
A			FROM FINISH DISCHARGING OR COMPLETION OF DISCHARGING DAMAGE REPAIRS TO BEGINNING OF PASSAGE "A" (EXCLUDING OFF HIRE PERIOD)		
B					
C					
D			DURING LOADING AT............		
E			" " AT............		
F					
G			FROM END OF LAST PASSAGE TO FINISH DISCHARGING OR COMPLETION OF DISCHARGING DAMAGE REPAIRS		
H					
Panama Canal Atlantic to Pacific					
Panama Canal Pacific to Atlantic					
TOTALS					

SUMMARY OF FUEL CONSUMPTION

	Fuel oil	Diesel oil
TOTAL ON PASSAGES		
TOTAL DURING DETENTIONS		
TOTAL IN PORT		
TOTAL CONSUMED ON VOYAGE		

SUMMARY (BBLS.)

Remaining from Voyage No...........		
Received at		
" "		
" "		
" "		
Total remaining and received		
Consumed during off hire (See "Remarks")		
Consumed on voyage		
Remaining at end of Voyage No. (BBLS.)		

REPORT OF FUEL

Fuel oil remaining	Fuel oil received	Fuel oil received
From last voyage	At	At
	Date	Date
Temperature	Temperature	Temperature
Gravity API @ 60° F	Gravity API @ 60° F	Gravity API @ 60° F
Quality	Quality	Quality
Grade (Name)	Grade (Name)	Grade (Name)
Viscosity	Viscosity	Viscosity
Fuel oil received	Fuel oil received	Fuel oil received
At	At	At
Date	Date	Date
Temperature	Temperature	Temperature
Gravity API @ 60° F	Gravity API @ 60° F	Gravity API @ 60° F
Quality	Quality	Quality
Grade (Name)	Grade (Name)	Grade (Name)
Viscosity	Viscosity	Viscosity
Report on Quality of Fuel		

EXHIBIT II

DETAILED CONSUMPTION OF OILS AND STORES

STORES		Remains from last voyage	RECEIVED		Total remaining and received	Consumed in port	Consumed on passages	Total consumed	Total remaining
			At	At					
Turbine Oil	Gal.								
Ice Machine Oil	"								
Diesel Engine Lubricating Oil	"								
Cylinder Oil	"								
Telemotor	"								
Diesel Engine Fuel Oil	"								
Kerosene	"								
Grease for Ball Bearings	Lbs.								
" " Winch Gears	"								
" " Deck Fittings	"								
" Rust Preventative	"								
Freon	Cylinders								
Wiping Rags	Lbs.								

CHIEF ENGINEER'S VOYAGE REPORT

33

Ship to fill in entire report. Current local time of the port is to be used.

VOYAGE PORT LOG

EXHIBIT III

Vessel	Class	Voyage No.	Date

Port	Pier	Cargo No.

OPERATION		DRAFT OF VESSEL			WATER		
		Fwd.	Aft	Mean			
☐ Loading	Arrival						
☐ Discharging	Sailing				☐ Fresh	☐ Partly Fresh	☐ Salt

VESSEL MOVEMENTS	DATE	TIME	ELAPSED TIME			CAUSE OF DELAY
			Days	Hrs.	Min.	
Passage Finished at			—	—	—	
Arrived at						
Pratique Given						
First Docking Tide After Pratique						
Left for Berth						
Alongside and/or Moored						
Started Loading or Discharging						
Finished Loading or Discharging						
First Undocking Tide after Finish Disc.						
Discharging Damage Reprs. Completed						
First Undocking Tide after Reprs. Comp.						
Left Berth						
Tugs Dismissed						
Anchored at						
Left Anchorage						
Passage Starts at						
TOTAL TIME IN PORT						

	DATE	TIME		DATE	TIME
Reported to Customs			Notice of Readiness Given		
Entered at Custom House			Customs Clearance Received		

DETAILS OF LOADING OR DISCHARGING

DATE	STARTED AT TIME	STOPPED AT TIME	ACT. TIME USED		TIME LOST		GROSS TONS	CAUSE OF DELAY
			Hrs.	Min.	Hrs.	Min.		
TOTAL								

(over)

34

EXHIBIT III

BUNKERING (Show quantity of Bunkers in bbls. of 42 gals.)

NAME OF BARGE OR PIER	ARRIVED		STARTED		FINISHED		DEPARTED		QUANTITY RECEIVED
	Date	Time	Date	Time	Date	Time	Date	Time	

Bunkers on Arrival	Bunkered	Total		Used in Port	On Sailing

LOADING STORES (Other than by crew)

	ARRIVED		STARTED		FINISHED		DEPARTED		QUANTITY RECEIVED
	Date	Time	Date	Time	Date	Time	Date	Time	

TUG SERVICE

NAME OF TUGS	ARRIVED		DEPARTED		DESCRIPTION OF SERVICE PERFORMED
	Date	Time	Date	Time	

REMARKS

Examined and Approved	Certified Correct
CAPTAIN	CHIEF OFFICER

3 5

PANAMA CANAL TRANSIT LOG

EXHIBIT IV

Ship to fill in entire report. Current local time of the port to be used.

Vessel		Voyage No.		Date	

WATER		DRAFT OF VESSEL			
			Fwd.	Aft.	Mean
		Draft arriving Colon/Balboa			
☐ Fresh ☐ Partly Fresh ☐ Salt		Draft leaving Balboa/Colon			

VESSEL MOVEMENTS (Delete not Applicable)	Date	Time	ELAPSED TIME			CAUSE OF DELAY
			Days	Hrs.	Min.	
Arrived Colon/Balboa Light Abeam						
Anchored						
Received Pratique						
Pilot on Board						
Arrived Oil Dock						
Left Oil Dock						
Started Transit						
Entered Gatun/Miraflores Locks						
Cleared Gatun/Miraflores Locks						
Passed Gamboa/Entered Pedro Miguel						
Passed Pedro Miguel/Cleared Pedro Miguel						
Entered Pedro Miguel/Passed Pedro Miguel						
Cleared Pedro Miguel/Passed Gamboa						
Entered Miraflores/Gatun Locks						
Cleared Miraflores/Gatun Locks						
Arrived Balboa/Colon						
Arrived Oil Dock						
Left Oil Dock						
Discharged Pilot						
Passed Balboa/Colon Light Abeam						
TOTAL TIME IN TRANSIT						

BUNKERING (Oil In bbls. of 42 gals.)

NAME OF BARGE OR PIER	ARRIVED		STARTED		FINISHED		DEPARTED		QUANTITY RECEIVED
	Date	Time	Date	Time	Date	Time			
Bunkers on Arrival	Bunkered		Total		Used in Canal		Sailing		

TUG SERVICE

NAME OF TUGS	ARRIVED		DEPARTED		DESCRIPTION OF SERVICE PERFORMED
	Date	Time	Date	Time	

REMARKS

Examined and Approved	Entries Certified to be Correct
CAPTAIN	CHIEF OFFICER

LAY—UP PORT LOG

Ship to fill in entire report. Current
local time of the port is to be used.

EXHIBIT V

Vessel	Between Voyage No._____ & Voy. No._____	Date
Port	During Voy. No._____	Yard

Cause of Lay-up

VESSEL MOVEMENTS (Delete not Applicable)	DATE	TIME	ELAPSED TIME			CAUSE OF DELAY
			Days	Hrs.	Min.	
Finished loading/discharging/passage (see foot note)						
Loading or discharging damage repairs completed						
Lay up repairs finished if completed at berth						
Left berth for repair yard						
Arrived at . . . . Repair Yard						
On dry dock (first docking)						
Off dry dock						
On dry dock (second docking)						
Off dry-dock						
Lay-up rep's finished if completed at repair yard						
TOTAL LAY UP TIME						
Left berth or repair yard						
Anchored at						
Left anchorage						
Passage starts at						
PORT TIME						

			DRAFT OF VESSEL			
			Dry Docking	Fwd.	Aft	Mean
Customs clearance received						
			WATER			
			☐ Fresh	☐ Partly Fresh		☐ Salt

LUBRICATING OILS CONSUMED DURING LAY-UP

Engine oil . . . . Gal.
Turbine oil . . . . Gal.
Cylinder oil . . . . Gal.

NOTE:—Time of finishing passage to be shown if vessel does not load or discharge cargo prior to lay-up.

EXHIBIT V   BUNKERING (Show quantity of Bunkers in bbls. of 42 gals.)

NAME OF BARGE OR PIER	ARRIVED		STARTED		FINISHED		DEPARTED		QUANTITY RECEIVED
	Date	Time	Date	Time	Date	Time	Date	Time	

Bunkers at Beginning of Lay-up	Bunkered		Total			Used during Lay-up		At end of Lay-up	

LOADING STORES (Other than by crew)

	ARRIVED		STARTED		FINISHED		DEPARTED		QUANTITY RECEIVED
	Date	Time	Date	Time	Date	Time	Date	Time	

TUG SERVICE

NAME OF TUGS	ARRIVED		DEPARTED		DESCRIPTION OF SERVICE PERFORMED
	Date	Time	Date	Time	

REMARKS

Examined and Approved	Certified Correct
CAPTAIN	CHIEF OFFICER

Every set of voyage abstracts must be designed to present a complete nautical and technical record of the voyage. Although the port, canal-transit, and lay-up logs circulate independently, they form an integral part of the deck abstract log. Some operations may allow for these separate logs to be tear-off pages within a deck abstract log. The passages must be shown in a prescribed manner in the deck and engine abstracts in conformance with separate specific instructions. Whenever a passage is interrupted by a port-time, canal-transit, or lay-up period, the record continues on the appropriate form. Since abstract logs are like pages taken out of a vessel's logbook, great care needs to be exercised to eliminate differences and omissions.

ABSTRACT LOGS: SHORT FORM

The separate deck and engine abstract logs (long form) are still time-consuming and somewhat complicated. Moreover, they do not appeal to the small operator.

Exhibit VI shows a combined deck and engine abstract log designed to expedite matters and appeal to those who may find the information sufficient for their purposes. This short form also needs the support of port, canal-transit, and/or lay-up logs. This simplified form eliminates a great deal of the technical record. If there should be any need to study the omitted data, however, this can still be done. Needless to say, this short form is bound to find favor with those who are required to complete and approve the log entries.

It will be seen later that this combined form of a voyage abstract (with port logs) embraces all the data required for a complete analysis of a voyage.

VOYAGE TIME SHEET

Upon receipt of the voyage abstracts, the office analyst may first prepare a "time sheet." Exhibit VII outlines the suggested form and lay-out. When the vessel's itinerary varies and a printed form is not practical, the time sheet may be set out on a blank sheet of paper. This step represents a useful and quick method of arriving at the main features of the voyage; in many cases, this is all the accounting department may need for costing purposes.

PERFORMANCE WORK SHEETS

Performance work sheets, shown in Exhibit VIII, were designed to facilitate the manipulation of the vessel-voyage data for the

EXHIBIT VI

DECK AND ENGINE ABSTRACT LOG

VESSEL: .... CLASS: .... VOY. NO.: .... TRADE: .... CARGO: .... G.T. ....

	VOYAGE REPORT (Delete not Applicable)		DATE & TIME	DISTANCE Miles	FUEL (Bbls)		CONS	REVOLUTIONS OR COUNTER	IHP OR SHP	WEATHER WIND FORCE	DETENTION/OFF-HIRE					REMARKS
					R'CVD	ABOARD					TIME Hrs	DIST Miles	FUEL Bbls	DRAFT		
1	START OF VOYAGE															PORT LOG
	END OF															
2	PASSAGE – A –	Sailed														
		Arrived														
3	PASSAGE – B –	Sailed														
		Arrived														
4	CANAL TRANSIT	Sailed														TRANSIT LOG
		Arrived														
5	PASSAGE – –	Sailed														
		Arrived														
6	LOADING P O R T															PORT LOG
7	PASSAGE – –	Sailed														
		Arrived														
8	CANAL TRANSIT	Sailed														TRANSIT LOG
		Arrived														
9	PASSAGE – –	Sailed														
		Arrived														
10	END OF VOYAGE															PORT LOG
	END OF															
11		TOTALS														

FUEL .... BBLS - ON .... FOR VOY. NO. .... API .... FUEL .... BBLS - ON .... FOR VOY. NO. .... API ....

MASTER: .... CHIEF OFFICER: .... CHIEF ENGINEER: .... DATE: ....

NOTE: Use other side for any additional information.

40

VOYAGE TIME SHEET

EXHIBIT VII

START: _____

FINISH: _____

S/S _____ VOY. _____

CLASS _____

DETENTIONS REPAIRS OFF-HIRE		PORTS	TIME	DIST.	FUEL	TIME CHECK
PORT						
PASS "A" DETENTION		BAY BALLAST "A"				
PASS "B" TIME ADJ.		SEA BALLAST "B"				
PASS "C" DETENTION		SEA BALLAST "C"				
PASS "D" DETENTION		RIVER BALLAST "D"				ROUND VOYAGE TIME
PORT		RIVER LOADED "E"				FUEL INVENTORY (BBLS)
PASS "E" DETENTION		BAY LOADED "F"				ON HAND BUN- KERED / CONS
PASS "F" DETENTION		SEA LOADED "G"				REPAIRS
PORT		BAY LOADED "H"				END VOYAGE
PASS "G" DETENTION		DETENTIONS A- B- C- D-				REMARKS
PASS "H" DETENTION		E- F- G- H-				
PORT		TOTALS				

41

EXHIBIT VIII

PERFORMANCE WORK SHEETS

VESSEL: CLASS: TRADE: YEAR: **PAGE 1**

MONTH	VOY.	LAY-UP TIME	TIME IN DAYS:							
			L'DG	D'SCHG	BAY	CANAL	SEA BALL.	SEA LOAD	DETEN	TOTAL
1	2	3	4	5	6	7	8	9	10	
3	5	11	12	13	14	15	16	17	18, 4	

PAGE 2

LAY-UP	FUEL CONSUMPTION									LUBRICANTS	
CONS	L'DG	D'SCHG	BAY	CANAL	SEA BALL.	SEA LOAD	DETEN	TOTAL	TURBINE	OTHER
11	12	13	14	15	16	17	18	19	20	21
	25		26	28	28	29	30	31	37	38

VESSEL: CLASS: TRADE: YEAR: **PAGE 3**

MONTH	VOY.	HOURS:				DISTANCE:			SEA BALLAST		
		BAY	SEA BALL.	SEA LOAD	SEA TOTAL	PORT	BAY	CANAL	OBS	ENG	DIFF.
	22	23	24	25	26	27	28	29	30	31	32
	3						19	20			

42

EXHIBIT VIII

PERFORMANCE WORK SHEETS

SEA LOADED			TOTAL STEAMING			DETEN-TION	TOTAL DISTANCE
OBS	ENG	DIFF	OBS	ENG	DIFF		
33	34	35	36	37	38	39	40
						22	6, 23

VESSEL: CLASS: TRADE: YEAR:

MONTH	VOY.	REVOLUTIONS				CARGO GROSS TONS
		BAY	SEA BALLAST	SEA LOADED	TOTAL STEAMING	
	41	42	43	44	45	46
	3					7

SHIP/HOURS		POUNDS OF FUEL:	
SEA BALLAST	SEA LOADED	SEA BALLAST	SEA LOADED
47	48	49	50

43

purpose of analysis. The vessel's abstract logs and the voyage time sheet provide the information that is entered here. A set of work sheets needs to be kept for each vessel and each class of vessels. The maintenance of such work sheets permits the calculation of to-date vessel and fleet averages at regular intervals.

COMPARATIVE VESSEL PERFORMANCE STATEMENT

This statement, shown in Exhibit IX, goes into the authorized distribution as the final statistical expression of the completed voyages in a given period of time. Whenever possible, a monthly or quarterly statement of this kind, showing current and to-date completed voyages in a given trade, is recommended. Obviously, the comparative statement's number of columns is closely related to the size of the operation (that is, the number of vessels employed and the length of voyages), and so is the interval of time at which this statement should be issued.

Under certain conditions, a standard performance may be calculated and made a permanent feature of the comparative performance statement for each particular trade and class of vessels. The procedure will be examined in the next chapter. The back of the form may carry voyage itineraries and other items of interest such as weather conditions, vessel's draft, the last drydocking date, and names of the master and chief engineer.

/S . . . . IN . . . . TRADE

EXHIBIT IX   VESSEL ITINERARY FOR VOYAGE NO. . . . . . .

MASTER: . . . . CHIEF ENGINEER: . . . .

CARGO	PORT	ACTIVITY	WEATHER (a)	ARRIVED	DRAFT	SAILED	DRAFT
				(b)			
						(c)	

(a) Wind direction and force (Beaufort Scale)
(b) End of . . . . ; start of Voy . . . .
(c) Finished . . . . ; end of Voy . . . .
    Date of last drydocking . . . .

COMPARATIVE VESSEL PERFORMANCE STATEMENT EXHIBIT IX

CLASS . . . . TRADE

		STANDARD		
1				
2	NAME OF VESSEL	STANDARD		
3	No. of Voyage or Completed Voyages			
4	Total No. of Voyage Days			
5	Total No. of Lay-Up Days			
6	Total Distance (Nautical Miles)			
7	Total Cargo (Gross Tons)			
8	Average Cargo			
9	Admiralty Coefficient - loaded			
10	Fuel Coefficient - loaded			
	VOYAGE TIME (24 Hr. Days):			
11	Ports ⎱ Loading			
12	⎰ Discharging			
13	Bay and river passages			
14	Canal passages			
15	Sea passages - ballast			
16	Sea passages - loaded			
17	Detention on passages			
18	Round voyage			
	DISTANCE (Nautical Miles):			
19	Port, bay, and river passages			
20	Canal passages			
21	Sea passages			
22	Detention on passages			
23	Round Voyage			
24	Miles per sea day			
	FUEL CONSUMPTION (Bbls):			
25	Ports			
26	Bay and river passages			
27	Canal passages			
28	Sea passages - ballast			
29	Sea passages - loaded			
30	Detention on passages			
31	Round voyage			
32	Avg. daily sea consumption - ballast			
33	Avg. daily sea consumption - loaded			
34	Avg. daily port consumption			
35	Fuel per observed sea mile - loaded			
36	Eng. sea miles per bbl. - loaded			
37	Lubricating ⎪ Turbine Oil			
38	Oil (Gals): ⎪ Other Oils			
	Speed (Knots):			
39	Sea passages - ballast			
40	Sea passages - loaded			
41	Round voyage (Sea passages only)			
42	Round voyage (Incl. bay and river)			
	Revolutions Per Minute:			
43	Sea passages - ballast			
44	Sea passages - loaded			
45	Round voyage (Incl. bay and river)			
	Percentage of Propeller Slip:			
46	Sea passages - ballast			
47	Sea passages - loaded			
48	Round voyage (Incl. bay and river)			
	Shaft Horsepower:			
49	Sea passages - ballast			
50	Sea passages - loaded			
51	Lbs. of fuel/S.H.P./hr.-ballast			
52	Lbs. of fuel/S.H.P./hr.-loaded			

(Rows 39–52 marked as AVERAGES)

SUMMARY OF PORT OPERATIONS

Exhibits X and X-a show forms designed for the purpose of analyzing in some detail what happens on and to the vessel while she is in port. The breakdown reflects the information one finds in the port logs. As in the case of the comparative vessel-performance statement, current and to-date average results will require the support of specially adapted work sheets; the composition of such work sheets should not present any difficulties.

OTHER EXAMPLES OF VOYAGE ABSTRACT LOGS

Several other versions of vessel-voyage abstract logs have been reproduced in Appendix H. These clearly show that our suggested set of abstract log forms will not necessarily fit every steamship operation. The engine abstract, for example, must be adapted to the vessel's propulsion plant. Port operations and turnaround mean different things to the passenger liner, the freighter, the tramp, or the bulk carrier. Yet it is also clear that the differences are a matter of emphasis linked to specialized operations and do not preclude a standardized approach.

Of special interest is Esso International's set of voyage abstract logs accompanied by appropriate instructions for completing them. This company also favors a one-page combined deck and engine abstract log. Obviously, the need for a rapid data turnover was given careful consideration.

A voyage port log, prepared by the vessel, and the "agent's report," completed by a representative of the shipowner in the vessel's port of call, are almost identical in appearance and the information they carry. The latter can be used to verify the vessel's port log and often carries information not available to ship's personnel. It performs a useful function insofar as it controls and measures the effectiveness of the owner's representative in the loading and discharging ports. The current Esso International form and other versions of a port agent report are shown in Appendix H.

STANDARDIZED FORMS

In this study, we are proceeding from the premise that there is a basic, yet vital voyage-turnaround information common to all types of vessel operations. If this premise is accepted, there should be no difficulty in arriving at standardized data-collection and data-analysis forms that would fit any and all types of operation. The fundamental voyage data, as understood here, are the same whether

EXHIBIT X

SUMMARY OF PORT OPERATIONS
ANALYSIS OF TIME IN HOURS AND DECIMALS

TRADE		LOADING AT						CLASS
VESSEL AND VOYAGE								
ARRIVAL AT THE PORT	Date							
	Time							
Awaiting berth/docking orders								
Awaiting pilot/tugs								
Awaiting port clearance								
Awaiting daylight								
Inclement weather/surf/tide								
Holidays								
Vessel repairs								
Awaiting cargo								
Loading equipment repairs								
Steaming to berth (incl. mooring)								
(a) Moored to commencement								
(b) Miscellaneous								
ARRIVAL TO START OF LOADING —Total								
START OF LOADING	Date							
	Time							
Actual loading								
Shifting vessel/loaders								
Loading equipment repairs								
Changing mooring lines								
Awaiting cargo								
Meals								
Discharging ballast								
Inclement weather/surf								
Checking draft and trim								
(b) Miscellaneous								
START TO FINISH OF LOADING — Total								
FINISH OF LOADING	Date							
	Time							
Cleaning decks/securing hatches								
Awaiting port clearance								
Awaiting daylight								
Awaiting pilot/tugs								
Completing crew								
Vessel repairs								
Inclement weather/tide								
(a) Ready to sail to leaving berth								
Leaving berth to clearing port								
(b) Miscellaneous								
FINISH OF LOADING TO SAILING — Total								
DEPARTURE FROM THE PORT	Date							
	Time							
ARRIVAL TO SAILING — Total								
CARGO (Gross Tons)								
DISPATCH G.T. Per Hour	Actual loading							
	Start to finish of loading							
	Arrival to sailing							

(a) Excluding delays otherwise specified   (b) See reverse side for details

EXHIBIT X - a

TRADE		DISCHARGING AT								CLASS	
VESSEL AND VOYAGE											
ARRIVAL AT THE PORT	Date										
	Time										
Awaiting berth/docking orders											
Awaiting pilot/tugs											
Awaiting port clearance											
Awaiting daylight											
Inclement weather/tide											
Holidays											
Steaming to berth (incl. mooring)											
Awaiting d'ging berth & shifting											
(a) Moored to commencement											
(b) Miscellaneous											
ARRIVAL TO START OF DISCHARGING — Total											
START OF DISCHARGING	Date										
	Time										
Actual discharging											
Shifting vessel/unloaders											
Discharging equipment repairs											
Oiling cranes											
Meals											
No work periods											
Inclement weather											
(b) Miscellaneous											
START TO FINISH OF DISCHARGING — Total											
FINISH OF DISCHARGING (* Indicates start of lay-up)	Date										
	Time										
Vessel discharging damage repairs											
Awaiting scheduled sailing time											
Awaiting port clearance											
Awaiting pilot/tugs											
Completing crew											
Inclement weather/tide											
Loading stores											
Vessel repairs (under 24 hours)											
(c) Vessel repairs (over 24 hours)											
Awaiting clear channel											
(a) Ready to sail to leaving berth											
Compass adjusting and calibrating											
Leaving berth to clearing port											
(b) Miscellaneous											
FINISH OF DISCHARGING TO SAILING — Total											
DEPARTURE FROM THE PORT	Date										
	Time										
ARRIVAL TO SAILING — Total											
CARGO (Gross tons)											
DISPATCH G.T. Per Hour	Actual discharging										
	Start to finish of discharging										
	Arrival to sailing										

(a) Excluding delays otherwise specified   (b) See reverse side for details   (c) Excluded from time in port

48

the vessel is a tanker, passenger or cargo liner, bulk carrier, or a tramp. Every ocean voyage consists of sea passages and port time; there may be bay, river, and canal passages in addition.

The extent and details of the practical application of a universally acceptable system of voyage-data analysis could very well be explored by the Maritime Administration, Maritime Cargo Transportation Conference (MCTC), possibly IMCO or, better still, by the industry itself. A joint committee composed of members of the American Merchant Marine Institute (AMMI) and the Society of Naval Architects and Marine Engineers (SNAME) would seem to be eminently qualified to investigate and recommend the proper course of action. A practical evaluation of the method presented here should embrace the pros and cons of having a standardized set of forms and instructions available to all ship operators the world over. Since it is quite possible that certain types of vessel operation may find adoption of the suggested method as their best course, while others may find it necessary to adapt it in order to make it workable, no one needs to wait for the conclusions of any deliberations that might be undertaken. The lack of standards did not prevent the spread of containerization and its allied developments. The customer's satisfaction comes first, standardization second.

Summary and Conclusions

This chapter has listed and briefly described suggested forms for the collection, analysis, and presentation of basic vessel-voyage data. The forms are suitable for the standard 8½-by-11 inches size paper, which permits the use of hard-cover, loose-leaf, ring binders.

No claim is being made that these forms represent the ultimate expression and readiness for standardization and universal acceptance. They may, it is hoped, provide a starting point and some solid ground towards this final goal.

In the next chapter the value of these forms will be put to a test of practical application.

CHAPTER IV

The Method in Practice

The success of a workable method or system can usually be traced to a comprehensive and clear-cut set of instructions, which at all times and in all situations provides a ready guide to action. Consequently, some discussion of the ground rules required to make our system work is in order before practical examples, suitably camouflaged and adapted, are brought in to illustrate the use of the forms briefly described in the preceding chapter.

LETTERS OF INSTRUCTIONS

To secure all-round cooperation and achieve a smooth-running operation, concise instructions should be available to all who fill out and analyze forms and reports. Such instructions must, of course, be kept up to date. Again, it would seem that a loose-leaf, ring-binder book offers the best way to do just that; new or amended instructions can be inserted while obsolete sheets can be removed. Two identical sets should be kept on board a vessel; one by the master, the other by the chief engineer. Other sets or pertinent extracts should be made accessible to various shore operating-personnel.

Aside from specific instructions that will determine and define, among other things, the start and the end of port time, lay-up, canal transits, and bay, river, and sea passages, a number of general instructions will usually be in order. Some of these deserve comment.

It is well to impress upon everyone that the information which goes into the abstract logs is of vital importance and that no effort should be spared to ensure its earliest possible arrival at the office. Work in a number of departments may be held up because these documents fail to arrive on time. The end of a month, or a quarter, or a year may add to the urgency.

Accuracy and legibility are of paramount importance. All erasures and interlineations should be prohibited. If an error is made in writing the entry, a line should be drawn through it and the correct entry made immediately thereafter.

Reasons for any delays, whether in port or at sea, must be stated clearly, and every effort should be made to determine the cause. Port-time delays require careful treatment and use of terminology. The relative importance of each delay, however small, must be retained; lumping together such items as awaiting scheduled sailing time, crew, weather clearing, tide, pratique, customs, clearance, etc., should be discouraged. Every time loading or discharging is stopped or resumed, the correct time and the reasons for stoppages must be given.

In certain trades the vessels may be faced with one or more critical arrival times. If a deadline cannot be met and idle waiting appears unavoidable, steaming at full speed may no longer be justified. In some cases the schedule may be adjusted for specific arrivals, pilots, canal passages, bridge openings, etc., that are purely dictates of operation. In general, however, saving of fuel and the elimination of any idle time should be the goal in maintaining optimum operating characteristics.

Lay-ups, repairs, and detentions should be clearly defined and separated, including the fuel consumed during these periods. Picking up and dropping pilots when entering and leaving ports are typical examples of detentions. A deviation or diversion should be looked at from the point of view of the overall passage. In most cases it is not enough to note the points of leaving and resuming the original course. The additional cost in terms of time, fuel, distance, and propeller revolutions must reflect the increase over and above the normal passage. The all-important question is how much more time, fuel, mileage, and revolutions were added to the normal passage through a deviation. It is clearly to everybody's advantage to have detentions and deviations correctly set apart from the normal voyage characteristics.

It may be helpful to distinguish among scheduled and unscheduled lay-ups, voyage repairs, and loading and discharging damage repairs. Anything over 24 hours may be considered a lay-up and excluded from the current voyage; a detention of less than 24 hours would remain in the voyage time. The suggested 24-hour cut-off time is, of course, quite arbitrary. It may be good practice to end a voyage and begin a new voyage or a lay-up upon completion of discharging. The time can be easily determined. Moreover, by then all the log abstracts, except for the final discharging port log, will have been mailed or deposited in the office. In this way there is a good chance that the last port log will be completed before the vessel sails, and handed to someone representing the office. There is always the outbound pilot who may be asked to mail the completed port log. There is no need to wait months, weeks, or even days for an analysis of a completed voyage.

The letters of instructions, or whatever they may be called, will, of course, be geared to a particular shipping operation. They will carry examples of completed log abstracts and other required forms. There is no reason why such an instruction manual should not embrace and expound also the policies of a company on any and all vessel or fleet operational aspects.

BASIC DATA COLLECTION FORMS

The voyage data used in the following example of an analysis of a voyage has been taken from actual experience. The procedure and calculations will be explained step by step. First, a brief look at the basic data collection forms that the master of a vessel completes and submits to the office.

Deck and Engine Abstract Logs. Exhibit VI-a shows a completed, one-page deck and engine abstract log designed to carry all the necessary information required to perform a complete analysis of the voyage. This report may be referred to as the "short form" as opposed to the "long form" consisting of the more complicated and separate deck and engine abstract logs.

Port Logs. Both forms of the deck and engine abstract logs, long and short, need the support of the pertinent port logs to make up a complete record of the voyage. Exhibits III-a and III-b provide the raw data for a detailed analysis of the port time in our hypothetical example. Had there been a canal transit or if the voyage was preceded by a lay-up, appropriate additional port logs would have been supplied.

AUXILIARY DATA COLLECTION FORMS

The manipulation of the basic data entered into voyage abstract logs requires a number of intermediary steps and auxiliary forms.

Voyage Time Sheet. Preparation of a time sheet (see Exhibit VII-a), which is nothing but a breakdown of each turnaround in terms of time, distance, and fuel, is not absolutely necessary. It is, however, a neat way of extracting and arranging the key information carried by the abstract logs. Moreover, it greatly facilitates the next step, namely, the transference of the voyage data to the work sheets for the preparation of the comparative vessel-performance statement.

EXHIBIT VI-a

DECK AND ENGINE ABSTRACT LOG
(SPECIMEN)

VESSEL: _____ CLASS: _____ "H" _____ VOY. NO.: 88 _____ TRADE: "A" _____ CARGO: BULK _____ 24,144 G.T.

VOYAGE REPORT (Delete not Applicable)	Sailed/Arrived	DATE & TIME	DISTANCE Miles	FUEL (Bbls) ABOARD R'CVD	FUEL CONS	REVOLUTIONS OR COUNTER	IHP OR SHP	WEATHER WIND FORCE	DET. TIME Hrs	DET. DIST Miles	DET. FUEL Bbls	DRAFT	REMARKS
START OF VOYAGE HOME		Feb 10 1000		1000		943 010						F-15'	PORT LOG
END OF DISCHARGING				4500								A-20'	
PASSAGE -A- From BAY	Sailed	1200	17		32	950 210		NE 3	0.05	-	1		Pilot Detention
To SEA	Arrived	1920	126		120	990 210							Time Plus 1 hour
PASSAGE -B- From SEA	Sailed	1923				1 575 663	12942	S 3-4					TRANSIT LOG
To PORT (Feb 15)	Arrived	0415	1780		1991								
CANAL TRANSIT From	Sailed												
To	Arrived												
PASSAGE From	Sailed												
To	Arrived			2									
LOADING PORT FOREIGN		1532		3356	51	1 577 663						F-13'	PORT LOG
PASSAGE -C- From SEA	Sailed	1532	1780			1 580 063	13073	NW 3-5	4.05	34	40	A-14'	Time Minus 1 hour Diversion
To BAY (2/20)	Arrived	0615			2116	2 207 080						F-33'	TRANSIT LOG
CANAL TRANSIT From	Sailed											A-35'	
To	Arrived												
PASSAGE -D- From BAY	Sailed	0620						NW 3	0.08	-	2		Pilot Detention
To PORT	Arrived	1550	126		148	2 250 822							
PASSAGE From	Sailed												
To	Arrived												
END OF VOYAGE HOME		Feb 21 1850	17	899	100	2 258 822						F-32'7	PORT LOG
END OF DISCHARGING												A-34'7	
TOTALS			3850		4558				4.18	34	43		

FUEL 4500 BBLS ON Feb 10 FOR VOY. NO. 88 API 13.65

FUEL _____ BBLS ON _____ FOR VOY. NO. 88 _____ FUEL _____ BBLS. ON _____ API _____

For VOY. NO. _____ February 21, 1964

MASTER: J. JONES CHIEF OFFICER: S. SMITH CHIEF ENGINEER: B. BROWN DATE: February 21, 1964

NOTE: February 17, 1964 - 1000 Position 20°N - 65°W - Distress call received - Changed Course
                    - 1403 Position.. - Resumed Course

Deviation: Time - 4 hours 3 minutes   Distance - 34 miles
            Fuel - 40 bbls   Revolutions - 22,730

EXHIBIT III-a

Ship to fill in entire report. Current local time of the port is to be used.

VOYAGE PORT LOG

(SPECIMEN)

Vessel	VESSEL I	Class	"H"	Voyage No.	88	Date	February 15, 1964

Port	F O R E I G N	Pier	"Z"	No.	22

OPERATION		DRAFT OF VESSEL			WATER			
		Fwd.	Aft	Mean				
[X] Loading	Arrival	13'0"	14'0"	13'6"				
[ ] Discharging	Sailing	33'1"	35'1"	34'1"	[ ] Fresh	[ ] Partly Fresh	[X] Salt

VESSEL MOVEMENTS	DATE	TIME	ELAPSED TIME			CAUSE OF DELAY
			Days	Hrs.	Min.	
Passage Finished at FOREIGN	2/15	0415	—	—	—	First Bell (Engine)
Arrived at ANCHORAGE		0421			06	Awaiting Pilot
Pratique Given						
First Docking Tide After Pratique		0600				
Left ANCHORAGE for Berth		0521	1	00		Inclement Weather
Alongside and/or Moored		0536			15	
Started Loading or Discharging		0630			54	Awaiting Cargo - 18ᵐ
Finished Loading or Discharging		1347	7	17		
First Undocking Tide after Finish Disc.		1500				Cleaning Decks - 27ᵐ
Discharging Damage Reprs. Completed						Awaiting Pilot - 06ᵐ
First Undocking Tide after Reprs. Comp.						Completing Crew - 24ᵐ
Left Berth		1514	1	27		Inclement Weather - 18ᵐ
Tugs Dismissed						
Anchored at						
Left Anchorage						
Passage Starts at FOREIGN	2/15	1532			18	Full Ahead
TOTAL TIME IN PORT				11	17	

	DATE	TIME		DATE	TIME
Reported to Customs			Notice of Readiness Given		
Entered at Custom House			Customs Clearance Received		

DETAILS OF LOADING OR DISCHARGING

DATE	STARTED AT TIME	STOPPED AT TIME	ACT. TIME USED		TIME LOST		GROSS TONS	CAUSE OF DELAY
			Hrs.	Min.	Hrs.	Min.		
2/15	0630	0730	1	00				
	0830	0900		30	1	00		Awaiting Cargo
	0948	1000		12		48		Meal Time
	1027	1100		33		27		Equipment Repairs
	1125	1230	1	05		25		Shifting
	1257	1330		33		27		Inclement Weather
	1340	1347		07		10		Checking Draft
		TOTAL	4	00	3	17	24,144	

(over)

EXHIBIT III-a   BUNKERING (Show quantity of Bunkers in bbls. of 42 gals.)

NAME OF BARGE OR PIER	ARRIVED		STARTED		FINISHED		DEPARTED		QUANTITY RECEIVED
	Date	Time	Date	Time	Date	Time	Date	Time	

Bunkers on Arrival 3356	Bunkered	Total 3356	Used in Port 51	On Sailing 3305

LOADING STORES (Other than by crew)

	ARRIVED		STARTED		FINISHED		DEPARTED		QUANTITY RECEIVED
	Date	Time	Date	Time	Date	Time	Date	Time	

TUG SERVICE

NAME OF TUGS	ARRIVED		DEPARTED		DESCRIPTION OF SERVICE PERFORMED
	Date	Time	Date	Time	
TITAN	2/15	0510	2/15	0540	Docking
TITAN	2/15	1430	2/15	1520	Undocking

REMARKS

Examined and Approved	Certified Correct
J. Jones	S Smith
CAPTAIN	CHIEF OFFICER

VOYAGE PORT LOG

(SPECIMEN)

EXHIBIT III-b

Vessel	VESSEL I	Class "H"	Voyage No. 88	Date February 20, 1964

Port	H O M E	Pier "Y"	No. 1

OPERATION		DRAFT OF VESSEL			WATER	
		Fwd.	Aft	Mean		
☐ Loading	Arrival	32' 7"	34' 7"	33' 7"		
☒ Discharging	Sailing	15' 0"	20' 0"	17' 6"	☐ Fresh ☒ Partly Fresh ☐ Salt	

VESSEL MOVEMENTS	DATE	TIME	ELAPSED TIME			CAUSE OF DELAY
			Days	Hrs.	Min.	
Passage Finished at ABEAM	2/20	1530	—	—	—	
Arrived at ANCHORAGE		1602			12	Awaiting Pilot
Pratique Given						
First Docking Tide After Pratique						
Left ANCHORAGE for Berth		1620			18	
Alongside and/or Moored		1844		2	24	
Started Loading or Discharging		1855			11	
Finished Loading or Discharging	2/21	1850		23	55	
First Undocking Tide after Finish Disc.						
Discharging Damage Reprs. Completed		2050		2	00	End Voy.88 - Start Voy.89
First Undocking Tide after Reprs. Comp.						
Left Berth		2148			58	Completing Crew - 48ᵐ
Tugs Dismissed						
Anchored at						
Left Anchorage						
Passage Starts at ABEAM	2/21	2315		1	27	
TOTAL TIME IN PORT			1	7	25	

	DATE	TIME		DATE	TIME
Reported to Customs			Notice of Readiness Given		
Entered at Custom House			Customs Clearance Received		

DETAILS OF LOADING OR DISCHARGING

DATE	STARTED AT TIME	STOPPED AT TIME	ACT. TIME USED		TIME LOST		GROSS TONS	CAUSE OF DELAY
			Hrs.	Min.	Hrs.	Min.		
2/20	1855	1900		05				
	1930	2400	4	30		30		Meal Time
2/21	0015	0300	2	45		15		Equipment Repairs
	0305	0600	2	55		05		Shifting Unloaders
	0615	0800	1	45		15		Equipment Repairs
	0815	1215	4	00		15		Meal Time
	1225	1300		35		10		Shifting Unloaders
	1315	1500	1	45		15		Meal Time
	1512	1700	1	48		12		Shifting Unloaders
	1715	1800		45		15		Equipment Repairs
	1815	1850		35		15		Equipment Repairs
TOTAL			21	28	2	27	24,144	

(over)

CHIEF OFFICER

EXHIBIT III-b BUNKERING (Show quantity of Bunkers in bbls. of 42 gals.)

NAME OF BARGE OR PIER	ARRIVED		STARTED		FINISHED		DEPARTED		QUANTITY RECEIVED
	Date	Time	Date	Time	Date	Time	Date	Time	
"CHIEF"	2/21	1400	2/21	1410	2/21	1600	2/21	1610	4600
									API
									15.0

Bunkers on Arrival 999	Bunkered 4600	Total 5599	Used in Port 130	On Sailing 5469

LOADING STORES (Other than by crew)

	ARRIVED		STARTED		FINISHED		DEPARTED		QUANTITY RECEIVED
	Date	Time	Date	Time	Date	Time	Date	Time	

TUG SERVICE

NAME OF TUGS	ARRIVED		DEPARTED		DESCRIPTION OF SERVICE PERFORMED
	Date	Time	Date	Time	
TACOMA	2/20	1615	2/20	1850	Docking
SACOMA	2/20	1820	2/20	1850	Docking
LACOMA	2/21	2030	2/21	2300	Undocking
RACOMA	2/21	2030	2/21	2200	Undocking

REMARKS

FUEL: Consumed - 100 bbls - to end of voy. 88
                          30 bbls - to Abeam
         Total   130 bbls

Examined and Approved	Certified Correct
J. Jones	S. Smith
CAPTAIN	CHIEF OFFICER

EXHIBIT VII-a

VOYAGE TIME SHEET
(SPECIMEN)

START:	FEBRUARY 10 - 1000	1964	S/S	V E S S E L I	VOY. 88
FINISH:	FEBRUARY 21 - 1850		CLASS	"H"	

		PORTS	TIME	DIST	FUEL	TIME CHECK		
DETENTIONS	17 - 14 - 03							
REPAIRS	17 - 10 - 00							
OFF-HIRE	04 - 03	HOME	0 - 02 - 00	17	32	1 - 16 - 17		
		FOREIGN	0 - 11 - 17	4	51		07 - 20	
						4 - 07 - 52		
	10 - 12 - 00	HOME	1 - 03 - 00	17	100	4 - 11 - 40		
	10 - 10 - 00		1 - 16 - 17	38	183		09 - 30	
	02 - 00						04 - 11	
PORT			1.678			11 - 08 - 50		
H O M E		BAY BALLAST "A"						
			07 - 20	126	120			
	10 - 19 - 23							
	10 - 12 - 00					21 - 18 - 50		
PASS "A"	07 - 23					10 - 10 - 00		
DETENTION	- 03		0.305			11 - 08 - 50		
	07 - 20	SEA BALLAST "B"						
			4 - 07 - 52	1780	1991			
	15 - 04 - 15					ROUND VOYAGE TIME		
	10 - 19 - 23					11.368		
PASS "B"	4 - 08 - 52		4.328					
TIME ADJ.	01 - 00	SEA LOADED "C"				FUEL INVENTORY (BBLS)		
	4 - 07 - 52		4 - 11 - 40	1780	2116	ON HAND	1000	
						BUN- KERED	4500	
	15 - 15 - 32		4.486				5500	
	15 - 04 - 15	BAY LOADED "D"				CONS	4601	
PORT	11 - 17						899	
F O R E I G N			09 - 30	126	148	REPAIRS		
	20 - 06 - 15						-	
	15 - 15 - 32					END VOYAGE	899	
PASS "C"	4 - 14 - 43		0.396					
TIME ADJ.	01 - 00	DETENTIONS				REMARKS		
DIVERSION	4 - 15 - 43	"A"	0 - 00 - 03	-	1			
	04 - 03	"B"	-	-	-			
	4 - 11 - 40	"C"	0 - 04 - 03	34	40			
	20 - 15 - 50	"D"	0 - 00 - 05	-	2			
	20 - 06 - 15		0 - 04 - 11	34	43			
PASS "D"	09 - 35							
DETENTION	- 05		0.175					
	09 - 30	TOTALS						
			11 - 08 - 50	3884	4601			
	21 - 18 - 50		11.368					
	20 - 15 - 50							
PORT	1 - 03 - 00	Diversion: Distress Call - Course Changed						
H O M E								

Performance Work Sheets. The purpose of keeping running work sheets (see Exhibit VIII-a) is self-evident; this is the only way of keeping totals and thus arriving at averages. A set of work sheets is required for each vessel. All vessels that represent a certain class, that is, are similar, will contribute to a "class" average performance, which needs the support of a separate set of work sheets.

Most of the preparatory and ancillary work in analyzing one or more voyages is done at this stage. If time sheets are not kept, then the breakdown of time, distance, and fuel consumption, as well as all other necessary data, must be extracted directly from the abstract logs. This work can be greatly facilitated by the use of a good calculating machine and specially adapted conversion tables. A set of such tables has been included in Appendix B.

The conversion of voyage time and its components into days and decimal parts of a day for entry into columns numbered 2 through 10 can be easily accomplished with the help of Table B-3 reproduced in Appendix B. Columns 23 through 26 provide for the respective bay and sea passages to be shown in hours and decimals of an hour; Tables B-1 and B-2 makes conversion easy.

Columns 11 through 19 carry the breakdown of fuel consumption. Columns 20 and 21 provide for the consumption of turbine oil and other lubricants such as cylinder, dynamo, crankcase, compressor, ice-machine, telemotor, and Diesel oils.

Columns 27 through 40 break down the round-voyage distance. The observed mileage is extracted from the abstract logs while its corresponding engine or propeller distance results from the multiplication of the number of propeller revolutions for a given passage by a constant (pitch of the propeller in feet divided by 6080 feet).

Columns 42 through 45 provide space for the entry of the number of propeller revolutions by passages. The weight of cargo carried by the vessel is entered in column 46.

Sea passages expressed in hours and decimals of an hour (see columns 24 and 25) multiplied by the corresponding average SHP developed by the engines gives the shaft horsepower hours to be entered in columns 47 and 48. Appendix C contains notes on the calculation of horsepower.

The conversion from barrels into pounds of the amount of fuel consumed, for entry into columns 49 and 50, involves the use of API degrees, a procedure explained in Appendix B under Table B-4.

EXHIBIT VIII-a

PERFORMANCE WORK SHEETS
(SPECIMEN)

VESSEL: VESSEL I   **CLASS:** "H"   **TRADE:** "A"   **YEAR:** 1964   **PAGE 1**

MONTH	VOY.	LAY-UP TIME	TIME IN DAYS:							
			L'DG	D'SCHG	BAY	CANAL	SEA BALL.	SEA LOAD	DETEN	TOTAL
	1	2	3	4	5	6	7	8	9	10
	3	5	11	12	13	14	15	16	17	18, 4
Jan	85	-	0.520	1.287	0.691	-	4.290	4.518	0.050	11.356
Feb	86	8.110	0.360	1.648	0.665	-	4.201	4.472	0.039	11.385
Feb	87	-	0.420	1.453	0.682	-	4.322	4.564	0.111	11.552
Feb	88	-	0.470	1.208	0.701	-	4.328	4.486	0.175	11.368
	4	8.110	1.770	5.596	2.739	-	17.141	18.040	0.375	45.661

PAGE 2

LAY-UP CONS	FUEL CONSUMPTION								LUBRICANTS	
	L'DG	D'SCHG	BAY	CANAL	SEA BALL.	SEA LOAD	DETEN	TOTAL	TURBINE	OTHER
11	12	13	14	15	16	17	18	19	20	21
		25		26	28	28	29	30	31	37	38
-	72	178	281	-	2009	2127	6	4673	27	1
80	51	233	292	-	2012	2136	11	4735	28	1
-	49	170	274	-	2037	2089	44	4663	42	1
-	51	132	268	-	1991	2116	43	4601	19	1
80	223	713	1115	-	8049	8468	104	18672	116	4

VESSEL: VESSEL I   **CLASS:** "H"   **TRADE:** "A"   **YEAR:** 1964   **PAGE 3**

MONTH	VOY.	HOURS:				DISTANCE:			SEA BALLAST		
		BAY	SEA BALL.	SEA LOAD	SEA TOTAL	PORT	BAY	CANAL	OBS	ENG	DIFF.
	22	23	24	25	26	27	28	29	30	31	32
	3						19	20			
Jan	85	16.58	102.97	108.43	227.98	38	252	-	1779	1804	25
Feb	86	15.97	100.83	107.33	224.13	38	250	-	1779	1751	-28
Feb	87	16.37	103.73	109.53	229.63	38	254	-	1779	1788	9
Feb	88	16.83	103.87	107.67	228.37	38	252	-	1780	1781	1
	4	65.75	411.40	432.96	910.11	152	1008	-	7117	7124	7

61

EXHIBIT VIII-a

PERFORMANCE WORK SHEETS
(SPECIMEN)

SEA LOADED			TOTAL STEAMING			DETEN-TION	TOTAL DISTANCE
OBS	ENG	DIFF	OBS	ENG	DIFF		
33	34	35	36	37	38	39	40
						22	6, 23
1780	1860	80	3811	3916	105	-	3849
1779	1827	48	3808	3832	24	6	3852
1779	1842	63	3812	3882	70	34	3884
1780	1838	58	3812	3874	62	34	3884
7118	7367	249	15243	15504	261	74	15469

VESSEL: VESSEL I   CLASS: "H"   TRADE: "A"   YEAR: 1964

MONTH	VOY.	REVOLUTIONS				CARGO GROSS TONS
		BAY	SEA BALLAST	SEA LOADED	TOTAL STEAMING	
	41	42	43	44	45	46
	3					7
Jan	85	82 722	593 045	611 545	1 287 312	24 045
Feb	86	83 628	575 457	600 705	1 259 790	23 832
Feb	87	82 658	587 713	605 591	1 275 962	23 925
Feb	88	83 742	585 453	604 287	1 273 482	24 144
	4	332 750	2 341 668	2 422 128	5 096 546	95 946

SHIP/HOURS		POUNDS OF FUEL:	
SEA BALLAST	SEA LOADED	SEA BALLAST	SEA LOADED
47	48	49	50
1 352 099	1 431 927	678 754	721 691
1 315 630	1 409 672	685 443	727 391
1 332 308	1 369 563	691 468	709 414
1 344 286	1 407 570	678 864	720 676
5 344 323	5 618 732	2 734 529	2 879 172

COMPARATIVE VESSEL PERFORMANCE STATEMENT

We are now ready for the final step, namely, the preparation of the comparative vessel-performance statement (see Exhibit IX-a), the heart of any vessel-performance analysis. For that reason, its presentation will be analyzed in some detail.

The form itself is designed to show all voyages completed in a given trade by one or more vessels within an agreed-upon period of time (this time period is closely related to the size of the fleet and operation). Details of the itinerary, names of the master and chief engineer, weather encountered, draft record, and the last drydocking date may be printed on the back of the form for ready reference, because they often may help to explain certain variations from the norm in the vessel's performance.

Standard Voyage Performance. A trade that offers little or no operating variations for vessels working that trade, produces ideal conditions for the establishment of a standard performance, which can act as a guide in assessing actual performance. The goals should be realistic but attainable only under ideal conditions. If a standard turnaround can be worked out, it should become a permanent but not inflexible feature of the performance statement. The use of color, like red, may increase its visual effectiveness.

Generally speaking, most vessel performances can be translated into standards on the basis of capacity, builders' specifications, shop tests, trials, and averages of previously observed performance. Purely scientific and statistical methods are also available, and one of them will be found briefly described in the last chapter.

The following remarks, intended to clarify the procedure for establishing voyage-performance standards, have been interspersed with bracketed numbers which relate to the numbered lines in the comparative statement (see Exhibit IX-a).

For various reasons, which have been made clear in Appendix E, cargo standards (7-8) cannot be reduced to a single figure.

The pros and cons of the admiralty (9) and fuel (10) coefficients can be gleaned from Appendix F. They are used mainly by the European shipowner; for him, fuel continues to be a relatively more important item in ship operation than in the United States.

The standard breakdown of the round-voyage time (11-18) reflects the recommended speeds (39-42), official distances (19-23), and previous average performances. Under "detention on passages" (17), sole allowance was made for picking up and dropping pilots in and out of the ports of call.

```
  V E S S E L   I                      "A"
/S........................IN........................ TRADE
```

EXHIBIT IX-a   VESSEL ITINERARY FOR VOYAGE NO. .88...   SPECIMEN

MASTER:....J. JONES.........................CHIEF ENGINEER:...B. BROWN.............

CARGO	PORT	ACTIVITY	WEATHER (a)	ARRIVED	DRAFT	SAILED	DRAFT
BALLAST	HOME	ORDERS	-	Feb 10 (b) 1000	-	Feb 10 1200	15' 0" 20' 0"
			NE-3 S-3/4				
BULK	FOREIGN	LOADING	-	Feb 15 0415	13' 0" 14' 0"	Feb 15 1532	33' 1" 35' 1"
			NW-3/5 NW-3				
BULK	HOME	DISCHARGING	-	Feb 20 1550	32' 7" 34' 7"	Feb 21 (c) 1850	15' 0" 20' 0"

(a) Wind direction and force (Beaufort Scale)
(b) End of .DISCHARGING.......; start of Voy .88.............
(c) Finished.....DISCHARGING.....; end of Voy .88.............
Date of last drydocking .November 15, 1963

CLASS . . . . "H" . . . .   (SPECIMEN)   . . . . . . "A" . . . . TRADE

1	VOYAGES COMPLETED IN - F E B R U A R Y - AND TO DATE - 1964			
2	NAME OF VESSEL	*STANDARD*	VESSEL I	TO DATE
3	No. of Voyage or Completed Voyages		VOY 88	4
4	Total No. of Voyage Days		11.368	45.661
5	Total No. of Lay-Up Days		-	8.110
6	Total Distance (Nautical Miles)		3884	15469
7	Total Cargo (Gross Tons)		24144	95946
8	Average Cargo		-	23987
9	Admiralty Coefficient - loaded	348.5	353.6	
10	Fuel Coefficient - loaded	9769.1	9703.7	
	VOYAGE TIME (24 Hr. Days):			
11	Ports Loading	0.434	0.470	0.442
12	Ports Discharging	1.138	1.208	1.399
13	Bay and river passages	0.660	0.701	0.685
14	Canal passages	-	-	-
15	Sea passages - ballast	4.253	4.328	4.285
16	Sea passages - loaded	4.490	4.486	4.510
17	Detention on passages	0.025	0.175	0.094
18	Round voyage	11.000	11.368	11.415
	DISTANCE (Nautical Miles):			
19	Port, bay, and river passages	288	290	290
20	Canal passages	-	-	-
21	Sea passages	3556	3560	3559
22	Detention on passages	-	34	18
23	Round Voyage	3844	3884	3867
24	Miles per sea day	406.73	403.90	404.62
	FUEL CONSUMPTION (Bbls):			
25	Ports	176	183	234
26	Bay and river passages	260	268	279
27	Canal passages	-	-	-
28	Sea passages - ballast	1970	1991	2012
29	Sea passages - loaded	2092	2116	2117
30	Detention on passages	5	43	26
31	Round voyage	4503	4601	4668
32	Avg. daily sea consumption - ballast	463.202	460.015	469.576
33	Avg. daily sea consumption - loaded	465.924	471.628	469.401
34	Avg. daily port consumption	112.000	109.181	127.070
35	Fuel per observed sea mile - loaded	1.177	1.189	1.190
36	Eng. sea miles per bbl. - loaded	0.888	0.877	0.869
37	Lubricating Turbine Oil	-	18	29
38	Oil (Gals): Other Oils	-	1	1
39	**Speed (Knots):** Sea passages - ballast	17.42	17.13	17.30
40	Sea passages - loaded	16.50	16.53	16.44
41	Round voyage (Sea passages only)	16.95	16.83	16.86
42	Round voyage (Incl. bay and river)	16.87	16.69	16.75
43	**Revolutions Per Minute:** Sea passages - ballast	95.90	93.94	95.36
44	Sea passages - loaded	94.40	93.54	93.13
45	Round voyage (Incl. bay and river)	94.55	92.94	93.42
46	**Percentage of Propeller Slip:** Sea passages - ballast	0.50	0.06	0.10
47	Sea passages - loaded	4.25	3.16	3.38
48	Round voyage (Incl. bay and river)	2.26	1.60	1.68
49	**Shaft Horsepower:** Sea passages - ballast	13030	12942	12991
50	Sea passages - loaded	13060	13073	12977
51	Lbs. of fuel/S.H.P./hr.-ballast	0.500	0.505	0.512
52	Lbs. of fuel/S.H.P./hr.-loaded	0.502	0.512	0.512

(Rows 39–52 marked **AVERAGES** in left margin)

Official sources (United States Hydrographic Office, for example) should be consulted in the compilation of standard distances (19-23). Detentions caused by pilots do not, as a rule, involve any additional distance. Average miles per sea day (24), the product of the total sea mileage (21) divided by the number of days at sea (15 plus 16), is an efficiency index; it may be used with some success for rating purposes.

Standard fuel consumption (25-31), as it corresponds to the port time and various passages, reflects the shipbuilders' trials and shop-test results modified by actual experience (see Appendix D). Fuel consumed during the time a pilot boards or leaves a vessel can be standardized. The total time in port and at sea, and the corresponding fuel consumption, yield useful daily averages (32-34).

Propulsion efficiency is reflected to some extent in the amount of fuel consumed per observed sea mile (35) and in the number of engine sea-miles covered per one barrel of fuel consumed (36). The difference between the observed and engine distances is caused by the slip of the propeller. In other words, the upward or downward movement of these two indices is closely linked with the slip of the propeller (46-48), which in turn reflects the weather conditions encountered, and roughness of the ship's hull. Dividing observed sea mileage (half of 21) into the corresponding fuel consumption (29) will produce fuel consumed per observed sea mile (35). Engine sea miles divided by the corresponding fuel consumption (29) will yield mileage per barrel of fuel consumed (36). As mentioned before, engine distance is the product of the total number of propeller revolutions for a given passage multiplied by a constant (divide the pitch of the propeller in feet by 6080 feet).

Consumption of lubricating oils (37-38) does not lend itself in most cases to the establishment of a standard.

A vessel operating guide, with trial data, graphs, and curves, serves as the main source of information for the establishment of the recommended average speeds (39-42), the related propeller revolutions per minute (43-45), and the average shaft horsepower (49-50) required to maintain the desired standard revolutions per minute and the speed.

The average percentage of propeller slip (46-48) is the difference between the observed and engine distances divided by the engine distance. It will be positive when the engine distance exceeds the observed distance; negative when observed exceeds engine distance. It is well to remember that the apparent slip of a propeller calculated with ship's speed is of little value except as a yardstick for indicating weather influences, bottom fouling, etc., in the same ship. With *different* ships and/or propellers, the slip is not a measure of efficiency; it is of no use to compare two propellers on the basis of the apparent slip.[1]

Any deterioration in the machinery output will invariably manifest itself in an increase in fuel consumption for a given power. The index to watch is the "lbs. of fuel/SHP/hour" (51-52) consumption figure, which, with the help of the official vessel operating guide, can be computed for the purpose of establishing a standard.

When creating or establishing a standard performance, it is important to keep in mind the interdependency and interrelationship of the various measures. They flow out of each other and depend on a few initial basic values and ingredients. A standard performance arrangement of this type can lead to the establishment of a fair and satisfactory rating system of vessels and their command.

Actual Voyage Performance. Our hypothetical example of an actual comparative vessel-performance statement (see Exhibit IX-a) for the month of February does not tell the whole story because of lack of space. The complete statement would show voyages Nos. 86, 87, and 88, followed by a monthly average for these three completions and a yearly to-date average for four completions.

When dealing with vessels belonging to a "class," i.e., sister ships, the monthly or quarterly average performance may be omitted in favor of a to-date yearly average for each particular vessel and a to-date yearly "class" average. Whenever a standard performance cannot be established or is not practicable, setting the vessel and class averages against each other affords some measure of comparison and may disclose certain trends that need watching or immediate action.

To be an effective and useful management control tool, the comparative statement must embrace a meaningful number of regularly completed voyages. The size of the statement and how often it should be prepared is determined by the inverse relationship between the number of vessels employed and the length (in time) of the voyage involved in a particular trade. With a fleet of, say, ten vessels turning around in about ten days, a monthly statement is called for. The same operation summarized quarterly would result in an unwieldy comparison. On the other hand, the same fleet faced with a 30-day trip could not be effectively compared on a monthly basis.

---

[1] K. Tasseron, "Some Remarks on the Slip and the Efficiency of Ship's Propellers," *Shipbuilding and Shipping Record*, London, March 5, 1959, p. 316.

It is a good rule to use the end-of-the-voyage date for determining the number of completions within the agreed-upon time span. The accounting department may want this rule to be somewhat flexible, especially at the end of a year.

Various factors—the absence of ballast runs, for example—may necessitate certain obvious adaptive changes in the statement and its legend. It may be advantageous to divide long voyages into outbound and inbound legs, each meriting separate treatment.

In order to get the feel of the procedure and calculations involved in the preparation of a vessel-performance statement, let us look at it line by line (see Exhibit IX-a). The numbers in parentheses refer to columns in the work sheets (see Exhibit VIII-a) which carry the pertinent source data.

1. Period of time covered
2. Name of the vessel or "class" of vessels
3. The number of the voyage completed and number of voyages completed to date (1, 22, 41)
4. Round-voyage time and total to-date number of voyage days (10)
5. Lay-up time and total to-date lay-up days (2)
6. Round-voyage distance and total to-date mileage (40)
7. Cargo carried on voyage and total to date (46)
8. Average cargo carried on voyages completed to date (46 ÷ number of voyages)
9. No provision has been made in the work sheets for this coefficient (see Appendix F)
10. No provision has been made in the work sheets for this coefficient (see Appendix F)
11. Loading port-time (3)
12. Discharging port-time (4)
13. Bay and/or river passage time (5)
14. Canal-passage time (6)
15. Sea-passage time: ballast (7)
16. Sea-passage time: loaded (8)
17. Detentions, deviations and delays (9)
18. Round-voyage time (10)
19. Distance: port plus bay and/or river passages (27 + 28)
20. Distance: canal passages (29)
21. Distance: sea passages (30 + 33)
22. Distance: deviation passages (39)
23. Distance: round voyage (40)
24. Mileage divided by time [(30 + 33) ÷ (7 + 8)]
25. Fuel consumption: ports (12 + 13)
26. Fuel consumption: bay and/or river passages (14)
27. Fuel consumption: canal passages (15)
28. Fuel consumption: ballast sea-passages (16)
29. Fuel consumption: loaded sea-passages (17)

30. Fuel consumption: detentions and deviations (18)
31. Fuel consumption: round voyage (19)
32. Fuel consumption divided by time: ballast (16 ÷ 7)
33. Fuel consumption divided by time: loaded (17 ÷ 8)
34. Fuel consumption divided by time: ports [(12 + 13) ÷ (3 + 4)]
35. Fuel consumption divided by mileage: loaded (17 ÷ 33)
36. Mileage divided by fuel consumption: loaded (34 ÷ 17)
37. Turbine oil consumption (20)
38. Consumption of other lubricants (21)
39. Speed in knots: ballast (30 ÷ 24)
40. Speed in knots: loaded (33 ÷ 25)
41. Speed in knots: sea passages [(30 + 33) ÷ (24 + 25)]
42. Speed in knots: round voyage (36 ÷ 26)
43. Propeller revolutions: ballast [(43 ÷ 24) ÷ 60]
44. Propeller revolutions: loaded [(44 ÷ 25) ÷ 60]
45. Propeller revolutions: round voyage [(45 ÷ 26) ÷ 60]
46. Percentage of propeller slip: ballast (32 ÷ 31)
47. Percentage of propeller slip: loaded (35 ÷ 34)
48. Percentage of propeller slip: round voyage (38 ÷ 37)
49. Shaft horsepower: ballast (47 ÷ 24)
50. Shaft horsepower: loaded (48 ÷ 25)
51. Pounds of fuel consumed per shaft horsepower hour: ballast (49 ÷ 47)
52. Pounds of fuel consumed per shaft horsepower hour: loaded (50 ÷ 48)

After an agreed-upon period of time, the work sheet data for a vessel or class of vessels is totaled column by column, checked and rechecked, wherever possible, across. Averaging calls for the use of a reciprocal of the divisor which represents the number of voyages. If this reciprocal can be locked into a calculator, a great deal of time-consuming division can be avoided.

Distribution of the comparative vessel-performance statement (which should include copies to the master and the chief engineer) would be accompanied by a covering memorandum or letter of transmittal which would highlight the achievements as well as the shortcomings in the overall picture.

SUMMARY OF PORT OPERATIONS

Port logs (see Exhibits III-a and III-b) provide the basic data for a detailed summary of port operations as shown in Exhibits X-b and X-c. What has really been done has been to take the loading and discharging port-time figures from arrival to sailing (as determined in letters of instructions) and give them a separate comparative-performance status. These statements may also show vessel to-date or "class" loading and discharging averages, which

EXHIBIT X-b (SPECIMEN)

SUMMARY OF PORT OPERATIONS

ANALYSIS OF TIME IN HOURS AND DECIMALS

TRADE "A"		LOADING AT FOREIGN						CLASS "H"
VESSEL AND VOYAGE		VESSEL I VOY 87	VESSEL I VOY 88				TO 2	DATE 4
ARRIVAL AT THE PORT	Date		FEB 15				MONTH	YEAR
	Time		0415					
Awaiting berth/docking orders								
Awaiting pilot/tugs			0 10					
Awaiting port clearance								
Awaiting daylight								
Inclement weather/surf/tide			1 00					
Holidays								
Vessel repairs								
Awaiting cargo			0 80					
Loading equipment repairs								
Steaming to berth (incl. mooring)			0 25					
(a) Moored to commencement			0 10					
(b) Miscellaneous								
ARRIVAL TO START OF LOADING —Total			2 25					
START OF LOADING	Date		FEB 15					
	Time		0630					
Actual loading			4 00					
Shifting vessel/loaders			0 42					
Loading equipment repairs			0 45					
Changing mooring lines								
Awaiting cargo			1 00					
Meals			0 80					
Discharging ballast								
Inclement weather/surf			0 45					
Checking draft and trim			0 16					
(b) Miscellaneous								
START TO FINISH OF LOADING — Total			7 28					
FINISH OF LOADING	Date		FEB 15					
	Time		1347					
Cleaning decks/securing hatches			0 45					
Awaiting port clearance								
Awaiting daylight								
Awaiting pilot/tugs			0 10					
Completing crew			0 40					
Vessel repairs								
Inclement weather/tide			0 30					
(a) Ready to sail to leaving berth			0 20					
Leaving berth to clearing port			0 30					
(b) Miscellaneous								
FINISH OF LOADING TO SAILING — Total			1 75					
DEPARTURE FROM THE PORT	Date		FEB 15					
	Time		1532					
ARRIVAL TO SAILING — Total			11 28					
CARGO (Gross Tons)			24,144					
DISPATCH G.T. Per Hour	Actual loading		6,036					
	Start to finish of loading		3,316					
	Arrival to sailing		2,140					

(a) Excluding delays otherwise specified   (b) See reverse side for details

EXHIBIT X-c   (SPECIMEN)

SUMMARY OF PORT OPERATIONS
ANALYSIS OF TIME IN HOURS AND DECIMALS

TRADE " A "		DISCHARGING AT H O M E					CLASS "H"	
VESSEL AND VOYAGE		VESSEL I VOY 86	VESSEL I VOY 87	VESSEL I VOY 88			TO 3	DATE 4
ARRIVAL AT THE PORT	Date			FEB 20			MONTH	YEAR
	Time			1550				
Awaiting berth/docking orders				0 | 30				
Awaiting pilot/tugs				0 | 20				
Awaiting port clearance								
Awaiting daylight								
Inclement weather/tide								
Holidays								
Steaming to berth (incl. mooring)				2 | 40				
Awaiting d'ging berth & shifting								
(a) Moored to commencement				0 | 18				
(b) Miscellaneous								
ARRIVAL TO START OF DISCHARGING — Total				3 | 08				
START OF DISCHARGING	Date			FEB 20				
	Time			1855				
Actual discharging				21 | 40				
Shifting vessel/unloaders				0 | 45				
Discharging equipment repairs				1 | 07				
Oiling cranes								
Meals				1 | 00				
No work periods								
Inclement weather								
(b) Miscellaneous								
START TO FINISH OF DISCHARGING — Total				23 | 92				
FINISH OF DISCHARGING	Date			FEB 21				
(* Indicates start of lay-up)	Time			1850				
Vessel discharging damage repairs				2 | 00				
Awaiting scheduled sailing time								
Awaiting port clearance								
Awaiting pilot/tugs								
Completing crew				0 | 80				
Inclement weather/tide								
Loading stores								
Vessel repairs (under 24 hours)								
(c) Vessel repairs (over 24 hours)								
Awaiting clear channel								
(a) Ready to sail to leaving berth				0 | 17				
Compass adjusting and calibrating								
Leaving berth to clearing port				1 | 45				
(b) Miscellaneous								
FINISH OF DISCHARGING TO SAILING — Total				4 | 42				
DEPARTURE FROM THE PORT	Date			FEB 21				
	Time			2315				
ARRIVAL TO SAILING — Total				31 | 42				
CARGO (Gross tons)				24,144				
DISPATCH G.T. Per Hour	Actual discharging			1,128				
	Start to finish of discharging			1,009				
	Arrival to sailing			768				

(a) Excluding delays otherwise specified   (b) See reverse side for details   (c) Excluded from time in port

EXHIBIT XI

VOYAGE TIMETABLE
(SPECIMEN)

TRADE . . . . . "A" . . . . "H" . . . . . . CLASS

	Day	Hour	Passage	Mileage
START OF VOYAGE (HOME)		1100	Port	
Leaving Berth		1200		17
End Port Time - Start Bay Passage	0	1400		
End Bay Passage - Start Sea Passage		2136	BAY "A"	125
	1			
Speed: 17.42 knots	2		SEA "B"	1778
	3			
	4			
Loading Port - Arrival	5	0341	Port	2
- departure		1406		2
	6			
Speed: 16.50 knots	7		SEA "C"	1778
	8			
	9			
End Sea Passage - Start Bay Passage		0152	BAY "D"	125
End Bay Passage - Start Port Time	10	1042		
Arrival Berth		1300	Port	17
END OF VOYAGE (HOME)	11	1100		3844

BREAKDOWN OF STANDARD PORT TIME

		Hours	Days
Start of Voyage to leaving Berth	)	1.00	0.042
Leaving Berth to End of Port Time	)	2.00	0.083
At Loading Port)		10.42	0.434
Start of Port Time to arrival Berth	)	2.30	0.096
Arrival Berth to End of Voyage	)	22.00	0.917
	Total	37.72	1.572

would require the maintenance of a set of appropriate work sheets.

It should be pointed out, however, that the port summaries consider time elapsed from arrival to sailing, while the comparative vessel-performance statement carries voyages that end upon finish of discharging the cargo. This precludes appending these summaries to the comparative statement since the time of issue or contents will rarely coincide.

VOYAGE TIMETABLE

A vessel-performance standard can be linked with what may be called a voyage timetable. An example, based on our hypothetical turnaround, is shown in Exhibit XI. This is done by choosing the most likely, most frequently occurring, or most desirable time of departure from the home port. Setting up an arrival-departure and start-finish voyage timetable is quite simple; speed to be maintained on various passages, a fine breakdown of port time, possible time differences, and a thorough knowledge of the trade and operations involved, are the required elements.

As a guide and aid in analyzing past as well as present and future voyages, a timetable of this kind has much to offer. The voyage standard and its complementary timetable are able to provide targets and make every voyage a challenge from start to finish, a challenge never exactly the same. The manual or letter of instructions appears to be the obvious place where such a timetable, one for every trade, should be made available.

SUMMARY AND CONCLUSIONS

This chapter has attempted to describe, with the help of an example, the step-by-step analysis of a completed voyage. To achieve clarity and simplicity, a straightforward, bulk-cargo-carrying operation was chosen. Although there was a lack of specific references and digressions in the narrative, it is hoped that the potential adaptability of this method to other, more complicated steamship operations was not lost upon the reader.

CHAPTER V

Economic and Practical Implications

General objectives need to be translated into specific goals that are meaningful to people in their day-to-day operations. These goals not only provide benchmarks for measuring progress, but are also a great aid in motivation and control.

Properly applied control is necessary to bring the results of operation in line with the established goals. The process of control requires the presence of three elements:

1. Standards that represent desired performance
2. A comparison of actual results against the standards
3. Corrective action

SETTING CONTROL STANDARDS

A satisfactory performance and the level of achievement or "par" need to be defined accurately. A complete application of standards to steamship operations would require an almost ironclad schedule and itinerary. Standard methods need standard conditions. The shorter and better organized the port time, the more conducive is the overall operation to standardization and a standardized method of analysis. More than anything else, it is the difference in the proportion of time spent at sea and in port that distinguishes one type of carrier from another. The following table attempts to present this division for various operations in very much rounded-off percentage figures; its usefulness centers about its comparative features.

TABLE 3

PERCENTAGE TIME AT SEA AND IN PORT
FOR VARIOUS TYPES OF VESSEL OPERATION

	Cargo Liner	Ocean Tramp	Passenger Liner	Tanker or Bulk Carrier	Container Ship
At Sea	40%	60%	65%	80%	90%
In Port	60%	40%	35%	20%	10%

The bulk carrier and the container ship both offer well-organized and well-defined port operations and voyage itineraries. The important thing, however, is that both the container and bulk carriage fit rather nicely into the way things are shaping up for the future of transportation. A systematic comparative analysis of voyage results will be an operational must.

In a standardized voyage-turnaround, a satisfactory performance determines the level of achievement and vice versa. Vessel-voyage-performance standards, as understood in this study, combine control over method as well as control over results. The complementary timetable, which sets out the standard voyage in terms of time and distance to be covered, is a good expression of what is meant by control over method.

Setting up voyage standards, as we have already seen, is not really complicated. A reasonably good standard can also be based on a statistical upper-quartile average, easily determined with the help of actual performance data collected over a period of time.

The scientific approach to the establishment of a vessel's standard performance favors the practice of setting aside a number of test days for taking careful measurements of performance over a limited period. Such routine may go a long way toward reducing the scatter generally found in data extracted from the usual log records. It is believed that suitable instrumentation coupled with strict discipline and liaison between the bridge and the engine room can produce usable data. Many believe that the ship's personnel should be given sufficiently clear indications of the object to be achieved, directed to the faults to be avoided, and then left a considerable degree of latitude in the exercise of their own initiative in connection with the methods of carrying out the tasks involved. Others disagree and claim that it may be advantageous to have the observer unaware of the eventual use to which the information may be put. Obviously, effectiveness is closely related to the interest shown by the shipowner.

For the statistically-minded, it is not difficult to ascertain a vessel's standard performance during the first months of her life by computing her regression equation. This equation represents the "exact" relation between speed, propeller revolutions, and delivered horsepower existing during a period of, say, ten weeks. In conjunction with shop-trial records that relate fuel consumption, revolutions per minute, and engine output, the standard-performance equation serves two purposes:[1]

---

[1] Ir. J. W. Bonebakker, "The Application of Statistical Methods to the Analysis of Service Performance Data," NECI, *Transactions*, 1951, vol. 67, p. 481.

1. It is the only means of checking accurately simultaneous records of fuel consumption, propeller revolutions per minute, horsepower, and speed as to their reliability, and of judging the fuel consumption per horsepower per hour. This should be of primary importance for an economic exploitation of the vessel; undue speed losses and excessive fuel consumption will at once become apparent.

2. By comparing horsepower and speed with the nautical conditions prevailing at the time, one can properly assess the loss of speed—or the excess of horsepower required to maintain speed—on account of the weather.

Strictly speaking, a ship's regression equation will be valid only under the restriction that the wake fraction (Taylor) remains constant, which implies constant speed, draft and trim, as well as roughness of the hull. None of these conditions is fulfilled in service. However, for the practical purposes with which we are concerned, the resulting inaccuracies are tolerable provided that the standard performance is computed from records collected during a period of limited duration and for a small range of speeds.

During each successive period, the vessel's regression equation should again be computed and compared with her standard performance. Analyses of service-performance data of several vessels have shown that the worsening of their performance due to fouling and the subsequent improvement after drydocking come out clearly. In this way the development of a vessel's performance can easily be supervised during her lifetime.

While doubtlessly correct that assessing wind direction and force is a matter of training and experience, a true description of the sea —direction, height, and length of waves and/or swell—is more often than not mere guesswork. Although the average values that can be obtained are sufficiently accurate for correlating speed losses with weather conditions and for classifying different vessels accordingly, the time may be ripe for some advancement in reliable weather-measuring instrumentation. If the marine industry makes a strong enough demand for such instrumentation, it will be forthcoming.

The relation of the main-engine performance to nautical conditions must reflect the fact that, in time, fuel consumption is bound to increase and the mechanical efficiency decrease due to wear and tear of all moving parts.

Abnormal changes in performance may have to be traced through a range of numerous possible causes. The result of these changes can be measured by analyzing service-performance data—of the logbook or "test-days" variety—or by making a series of runs over the measured mile. The latter method is both time-consuming and

expensive. Shell International, having found log entries both inadequate and too inaccurate for statistical analysis, installed aboard its
vessels reliable and accurate evaluation instruments to feed data
into automatic recording equipment. These records are then transferred to punched tape and sent by the ship's radio transmitter on
a new wide-band telegraphy channel to a computer in London.
Changes in the performance of ships at sea, it is claimed, can be
detected almost immediately; the causes of these changes can also
be isolated. Time will tell whether Shell International's approach to
service data collection is the practical solution; so far, little is
known of its cost aspect.

EVALUATION OF PERFORMANCE

The next step involves measuring the work that is done in terms
of the control standards and communicating the appraisal. Vessel-
voyage data, as has already been shown, is evaluated by comparing
actual performance with the established standards. Besides offering
a comparison of performance against standards, our comparative
vessel-performance statement, which is a kind of a control report,
will also reveal whether the situation is getting better or worse.
"To-date" and "class" average performances provide the trend
information.

Measurement of performance is of little value until the resulting
appraisals are properly communicated to people who can take
action. The task of reporting evaluation grows more complicated
with the number of people involved. There may be a need for control reports that summarize and communicate conclusions of the
measurements that have been undertaken. The highlights of a long
and involved comparative performance statement may be summarized in an accompanying memorandum or a covering letter to
satisfy the need for simplicity and presentation of key comparisons.

Control information should be sent immediately to the man whose
work is being controlled. This would certainly include the master
and the chief engineer.

RESPONSE TO CONTROLS

Controls are essential regardless of likes and dislikes. Negative
attitudes will be reduced when controls are understood to be simply
a means of spotting difficulties and keeping a record for reference
and planning. Sometimes participation can be a great help in secur-
ing acceptance of objectives, performance standards, and methods
of measurement.

Standards without a proper and rational dose of flexibility may become "unreasonable." How to introduce flexibility and still keep controls useful may not be an easy matter. The provision for "deviations and detentions" in our comparative vessel-performance statement fully satisfies the condition of flexibility by retaining the comparative feature of otherwise dissimilar voyages.

Practical experience has shown that the suggested controls in the form of a comparative vessel-performance statement have a good chance of being accepted as a valuable aid in getting a job done. Acceptance will produce and develop a healthy sense of rivalry among the vessels and their command. The routine job is no longer routine. In a short time the analyst may uncover clear evidence of efforts and measures leading to the maintenance of schedules, proper arrivals, and departures. Such analysis may lead to the discovery of the existence of a substantial margin where improvements can still take place. In one actual case history, the method described in this study was responsible for reducing an average turnaround in a well-established trade by a whole day. The analysis revealed certain practices that were eliminated as soon as they were brought to light.

Socony Mobil's recent study[2] and drive to reduce port time revealed that more time was lost on controllable delays than on uncontrollable delays, such as adverse weather, daylight and tides. The delays that could be controlled, or avoided, were: waiting for pilots, for tugs or barges, for berths, for tankage space, for stores and for customs clearance. An hour of such waiting is costing a Socony Mobil foreign-flag tanker $168. In 1963, the costs for such avoidable in-port delays soared to $2.3 million for the Company's foreign-flag fleet. It took three years of special research to uncover these areas where operation could still be tightened and costs reduced. With a good comparative method for analyzing vessel-voyage data, these possibilities for improvement would have been clearly and painlessly evident almost immediately.

The letters of instructions, which were mentioned earlier, play an important and self-explanatory part in fostering acceptance and cooperation; they lay the groundwork for controls. Each time a particular, but familiar, problem arises, this standing plan provides a ready guide to action.

---

[2] John P Callahan, "Oil Fleet Acting To Cut Port Time," *The New York Times*, February 21, 1965.

Appraising actual results against standards is often a guide in paying bonuses and may be a strong consideration in promotion. Round-voyage time, miles per day, and fuel consumption may serve as bases for a good rating system.

WORK STUDY APPROACH

In some respects, the suggested analysis of voyage results resembles the principle of work-study, which may be described as "the application of certain techniques of analysis and measurement to the processes of work with a view to their performance to the greatest possible advantage."[3] The objective, if not the technique, is the same; namely, to analyze down to the last detail what actually happens in the course of any overall operation, and to measure quantitatively the time taken for each bit of the operation so that we know and can record in suitable form all the elements that together make up the process. The counterpart of work-study in the world of paperwork is O & M (Organization and Methods).

The principles underlying both work study and O & M have been allowed full play in the suggested procedure and forms for vessel-voyage-data analysis.

STANDARD COST METHODS

Standard cost accounting principles provide an even closer parallel and resemblance to a comparative voyage-data-analysis system. There is a need for a thorough understanding of the use and application of standard cost methods in steamship accounting.

Cost accounting, generally speaking, considers three elements of cost—material, labor, and overhead—for the product or service rendered. Control of activities, which is the aim of cost accounting, may be enhanced through standard cost methods that provide yardsticks against which current operating results are compared and future ones forecasted.

The standard cost method determines a proper unit cost under normal operating conditions. If the actual cost is in excess of the standard, the excess is not considered a part of the cost of the service or product, but as a loss due to some inefficiencies. Thus, not only do standards provide a check; they also help pinpoint the reasons.

---

[3] D. McKenna, "Work Study in Transport," *The Journal of the Institute of Transport*, March 1959, vol. 28, no. 3, p. 93.

In place of unit-cost standards, steamship accounting requires standards of operating efficiency which may be classed under:

1. Vessel performance
2. Cargo handling
3. Overheads

The lack of widespread application of standard cost methods by steamship accountants may be traced to difficulties of establishing normal operating efficiency in a steamship operation. This becomes evident when it is realized that in the computation of such performance standards, one needs to consider a multitude of factors which enter into vessel operation, employment practices, and the disposition of expenditures not directly related to vessel operation.

It is claimed that an intelligent application of standard cost principles in steamship accounting will provide:

1. A guide for determining excessive costs in vessel performance, various segments of labor, and overheads.
2. A guide for planning future expansion or reduction of operations.
3. A basis for determining costs on completed operations for which actual accounts have not been received.
4. Guiding standards for freight tariff or labor negotiations.

All variances that exceed an accepted margin of tolerance must be carefully analyzed to determine whether the cause is an unusual or excessive expense, an increase in some phase of operating costs, or an incorrect standard.

The study of steamship accounting brings out the fact that although many segments of standard cost procedures are being used in the cost analysis of various companies, there has been no real effort to introduce a uniform system on an industry-wide scale.

The lack of any uniform system and the unexplored potential benefits provide a striking similarity in the current state of vessel-voyage-data analysis and standard cost accounting principles in the shipping industry. Furthermore, the complementary nature of the two concepts requires that they be viewed as interdependent. An application of standard cost principles, based and supported by an acceptable comparative vessel-performance analysis, offers the ultimate in control.

UNITED STATES MERCHANT MARINE AND THE SUBSIDY PROGRAM

The United States continues in a declining way to be a major maritime power. According to a count made public by the Maritime Administration on August 1, 1964, the American merchant marine has dwindled to 905 active ocean-going vessels, falling behind Great Britain (2,290 vessels), Norway (1,396 vessels), Japan (1,224 vessels), and Russia (1,002 vessels). As a trading nation, the United States occupies a place much closer to the top. We are clearly the world's leading international trader in terms of dollar volume.

For some 50 years prior to World War I, the United States played an insignificant role in foreign commerce. The development of a modern American merchant marine can be traced to both direct and indirect support of the industry by the federal government. The Shipping Act of 1916 introduced a program of government promotion, the nature of which was subsequently revised by the Merchant Marine Act of 1936. This act, with amendments in the interim, is still the basic legislation.

The 1936 act provides for direct subsidies paid to United States carriers in the foreign trade who enter into a subsidy contract with the government. These payments are designed to equate American costs, primarily of labor and vessels, with the cost of foreign operators and are known as *differential subsidies*. Less than half of the vessels flying the American flag are presently subsidized.

The responsibilities for carrying out the policies of the Act are lodged in the United States Maritime Administration, Maritime Subsidy Board, National Shipping Authority, and Office of the Maritime Administrator within the Department of Commerce. Under the Reorganization Plan No. 7, dated June 12, 1961, the regulatory functions were taken over by the Federal Maritime Commission, a separate and independent agency. The means that were placed at the disposal of these agencies for achieving the desired ends include:

1. Paying operating-differential subsidies to qualified operators serving essential trade routes.
2. Supporting the construction of new ships through:
   a. direct construction subsidies
   b. permitting subsidized operators tax deferments on earnings committed to new construction
   c. guaranteeing ship mortgages
   d. taking old ships in trade on new ones.
3. Extending cargo preference and other indirect support to American operators.

Coastwise and interstate trades are subject to United States Interstate Commerce Commission regulations for water carriers; the Treasury Department, with its Bureau of Customs, the Department of Agriculture, and other arms of government, also intervene.

Tanker, tramp, industrial, and domestic operators, because they do not meet some of the standards enumerated in Sections 601 and 605 of the 1936 act, do not qualify for operating-differential subsidies. Thus, for all practical purposes, the foreign trade liner operators are the only ones eligible. The construction subsidy, on the other hand, extends beyond the liner operators in foreign trade to those engaged in domestic commerce; American tramps and tankers are also included. These artificial props do not assure profitable operations. Support of the conference system, cabotage, and the requirement that defense cargoes and at least half the aid cargoes be lifted in American bottoms, contribute to this end.

According to one serious study,[4] the subsidy program and the subsidized merchant fleet make no substantial net contribution to the United States economy. This suggests the need for seeking and exploring alternatives to the present policies.

The subsidized operators must submit to a measure of supervision by the Maritime Administration. The greater the supervision, the greater the need for accounting detail. A uniform system of accounts, including a basic system of account classification, was established by the Maritime Administration in General Order No. 22, which also prescribes the forms (see Exhibit XII) to be used in reporting voyage expenses. The list of required reports includes:

1. A complete analysis of the round voyage after it terminates and all expenses have been recorded.

2. A quarterly analysis of wages, overtime, deductions, and contributions for vessel personnel.

3. A detailed analysis of fuel consumption by various vessels.

4. A detailed analysis of stores and supplies consumed.

5. A detailed presentation of feeding costs.

6. A detailed report of maintenance and repair costs by voyage.

7. A quarterly financial report, including all terminated voyages in detail, profit and loss statement, and the balance sheet.

The recipients of subsidies need to maintain a comprehensive program of cost analysis to properly prepare the various Maritime Administration reports. However, this cost analysis is not carried sufficiently into cargo-handling and a number of other voyage and port operations.

---

[4] Allen R. Ferguson and others, *The Economic Value of the United States Merchant Marine*, The Transportation Center at Northwestern University, Evanston, Illinois, 1961, *passim*.

EXHIBIT XII

Name of Respondent _____
SCHEDULE 3002A VESSEL OPERATING STATEMENT
FOR THE PERIOD _____

Line No.	Name of vessel					Voyage No.	Commodity
1							
2	Itinerary	1.	3.	5.	7.		9.
3	(Indicate ports of call for Bunkers)	2.	4.	6.	8.		10.
4	Service and type of vessel _____						
5	Number of voyage terminations _____			Number of nautical miles traveled _____			
6	Number of: Voyage days _____		Days at sea _____		Days in port _____		
7	Number of Passengers Carried:			Outward	Intermediate	Inward	Total
8	First class _____						
9	Cabin class _____						
10	Second class _____						
11	Tourist class _____						
12	Third class _____						
13	Other classes _____						
14	Total _____						
15	Number of freight payable tons of cargo carried _____						
16	(600) Operating revenue—Terminated voyages:						
17	01 Freight—Foreign _____			$		$	$
18	05 Freight—Coastwise and intercoastal _____						
19	08 Passenger—Foreign _____						
20	12 Passenger—Coastwise and intercoastal _____						
21	15 United States Mail—Foreign _____						
22	16 United States Mail—Coastwise and intercoastal _____						
23	17 Foreign mail _____						
24	19 Ad valorem _____						
25	20 Charter revenue (p. 59) _____						
26	24 Other voyage revenue _____						
27	Total vessel operating revenue _____			$	$	$	$
28	(700) Operating expense—Terminated voyages:						
29	Vessel expense:						
30	01 Wages—No. of crew _____ Straight time $ _____ Overtime $ _____			$ _____			
31	08 Payroll taxes _____						
32	09 Contributions - Welfare plans _____						
33	10 Subsistence - domestic $ _____ 14 Foreign $ _____						
34	15 Stores, supp. & equip. - Domestic $ _____ 24 Foreign $ _____						
35	25 Other maintenance expense _____						
36	35 Fuel—Domestic $ _____ Foreign $ _____						
37	40 Repairs—Performed domestic _____						
38	49 Repairs—Performed foreign _____						
39	55 Insurance—Hull and machinery _____						
40	57 Insurance—P. & I _____						
41	59 Insurance—Other $ _____ St. Lawrence Seaway $ _____						
42	60 Charter hire _____						
43	64 Other vessel expense _____						
44	Total vessel expense _____						
45	Port expense:						
46	65 Agency fees and commissions _____			$ _____			
47	70 Wharfage and dockage _____						
48	79 Other port expenses _____						
49	Cargo expense:						
50	80 Stevedoring—Domestic $ _____ Foreign $ _____						
51	*89a Installation of special fittings - (cost of material and labor) _____						
52	89b Other cargo expense _____						
53	Brokerage expense:						
54	90 Freight _____						
55	93 Passenger _____						
56	Other voyage expense:						
57	95 Canal tolls _____						
58	99 Other voyage expense _____						
59	Total voyage expense _____						
60	Total vessel operating expense _____						
61	Direct profit (or loss) from vessel operations _____						$ _____

84

The taxpayer, who pays the subsidies, would do well to insist that the present cost reporting and accounting in subsidized operations be married to a vessel-performance-data analysis of a type suggested in these pages. The Maritime Administration, since it has no way of relating costs to actual performance in all its aspects under the present system, cannot claim to know the true value and efficacy of the subsidy dollar.

The subsidy program, based on a standardized comparative vessel-performance analysis, would come much closer to its goal in the promotion of an efficient and even competitive United States merchant marine. It would not be difficult to separate the efficient operation from the marginal one and even less so from the inefficient enterprise, pinpoint the reasons, and then take appropriate action. The comparative vessel-performance statements yielding much statistical, technical, and economic data, would greatly aid government's research, development, and planning programs.

In non-subsidized shipping lines, the extent, character, and number of reports and analyses are strictly at the discretion of internal management. Intra-corporate relationships often influence such systems. Marine divisions of large oil companies, for example, will show conformance with the overall pattern of the parent corporation. Nevertheless, the majority of United States shipping companies remaining outside the subsidy program have adopted the Maritime Administration account classification. This would indicate that a possible nationwide acceptance of a standardized method for analyzing vessel-voyage data may very well depend on the attitude of the federal subsidy program.

Summary and Conclusions

This chapter examined the economic and practical aspects of determining standards that represent a desired performance and the subsequent evaluation of that performance. It was shown that the appraisals resulting from the comparison of the actual and the expected output must be properly communicated to the people whose work is controlled as well as to those who can take action. The response to controls may be closely linked with their flexibility and the amount of aid they offer in getting a job done. Too much flexibility, however, may leave the system of controls with its meat but no backbone.

The need to examine all details that make up a complete operation, as in the case of our comparative vessel-performance analysis, invites comparison with work-study and O & M. The need for control of activities also makes one turn to the principles of standard cost accounting. An application of standard cost principles, based and supported by an acceptable comparative vessel-performance analysis, merits study since this combination may offer the ultimate in control.

A possible nationwide acceptance of a comparative method for analyzing vessel-voyage data hinges on the attitude of the federal subsidy program. Under the present program there is no way to properly evaluate the efficacy of the subsidy dollar. The taxpayer, who pays the subsidies, would do well to insist that the present cost reporting and accounting in subsidized operations be married to a vessel-performance-data analysis of a type suggested in these pages.

CHAPTER VI

Research: The Big "R" in Transportation

Research is often confused with invention and development. Basic or pure research is the search after new knowledge of a broad and general nature which, when established, leads to technical or applied research. In transportation one usually has the latter in mind since the motivation is provided by potential solutions to specific problems.

The transportation system has grown into complex networks, and continued research is necessary for future perfection of transportation or logistics management. In the past, transport has operated successfully on a mixture of experience, intuition, and inspired hunches, but the future will find these qualities inadequate unless supported by accurate and comprehensive information properly collated and analyzed.

Knowledge of the transportation function and its use in the organization is the prime requisite of transportation research; the tools used are primarily those of mathematics, economics, and engineering.

Operations research provides an approach to methodology—the examination and arrangement of various elements in a system—and involves the study of situations in the field. The most commonly accepted definition of operations research is the application of the scientific method to the study of operations in order to come up with a quantitative basis for making decisions. The official language of OR is mathematics, a language most of us find alien and forbidding. Moreover, the techniques, skills, and terminology of OR—queuing theory (study of waiting lines), linear and non-linear programming, econometrics, CPM (critical path method), decision and game theory, Monte Carlo, operational gaming, a priori probabilities, etc.—can awe the uninitiated. Also, the practical application of most OR techniques depends on high-capacity computers and related technology. These techniques and procedures, exotic in

name, tend to draw attention away from the fundamental principles
of operations research. The scope of OR in the shipping world, and
the potential savings, are enormous.

Another powerful tool that has been placed at our disposal is the
"input-output" model, which can remove much of the guesswork
from vital areas of forecasting, planning, and operating. It is
called an input-output model (which is an array of numbers
arranged in the form of a grid) because each of the numbers in it
represents the amount of input from one industry, or commodity,
which is needed to produce one unit of output in another industry,
or commodity. Once set up on a computer, this simple table becomes a powerful tool to compute answers to the variety of intricate
problems facing businessmen and the government. The oil industry
has utilized input-output models extensively in improving the
efficiency of its operations. It has helped in the development, engineering and running of systems to assist top oil executives schedule
refining, transportation and distribution in their complex of re-
fineries, tanker fleets and distribution systems.

NEW TRANSPORTATION CONCEPTS

Although transportation generally and ocean shipping in particular is still largely a custom-encrusted business activity populated by
traditionalists and conservatives, complacency has been disturbed
by certain innovations, and the industry is more anxious than ever
to investigate new approaches. In vessel operation and construction,
set ways and outlooks may soon be a thing of the past. Hardly a
month passes without some evidence of initiative and inventiveness
being shown.

One of the major goals today is coordinated transportation which,
according to several authorities, will be commonplace in ten years.
This system, based on unit handling and intermodal routes, would
theoretically make it possible for a shipper to consign his freight
to any point in the world and have it delivered without rehandling
enroute. All the impressive advantages, such as one bill of lading,
the savings in paperwork and transfer delays from one mode of
transportation to another, and the reduction in pilferage losses,
have already been confirmed by integrated movements that have
ceased to be a rarity. The success of fully-integrated transport
services depends on the study and application of modern computerized techniques by management and operations.

Almost half of the total transportation cost is accounted for by
cargo-handling operations. This is certainly true of ocean shipping

where, in addition, conventional cargo-handling uses up almost half of the ship's time, which would otherwise be available for transportation per se. The improvement of productivity is the basic task facing steamship companies. The means of achieving higher productivity have been sought in containerization, palletization, mechanization of handling, specialization, shuttle operations, etc.

One of the toughest problems confronting the maritime industry, however, is the attainment of competitive efficiency through shipboard automation and crew reduction. This is being tackled without too much fanfare, and there appear to be hopeful and encouraging signs in this effort.[1]

Shipowners have shown little interest in construction savings stemming from shipbuilding standardization techniques. The practice is to build ships for the trade; it is said that specialized trades give no scope for standardization. This idea appears only recently to have been questioned by three large independent Swedish steamship companies that have collaborated in placing an order for six standardized cargo liners; this is certainly a new approach in ship designing and construction. More cooperative research into ship design might very well lead to substantial weight savings and layout improvements from which standardization might emerge. The United States Maritime Administration, convinced that ship standardization can reduce construction and possibly maintenance costs, proposed recently a new policy based on standardization of design for tonnage to be built with Federal aid.[2]

Some segments of the shipping industry claim that every aspect of marine transportation has been put under the microscope of research. The oil companies, because transportation is such a significant portion of the overall cost of petroleum, have led the way in transportation research. Almost alone, they have long recognized the importance of control standards and proper analysis of vessel-voyage data in day-to-day operations.

PLETHORA OF FORMS AND DOCUMENTS

When it comes to moving people and goods, forms and papers proliferate. Those engaged in ocean carriage have been coping with an ever-increasing mass of papers, forms, and documents. These include customs procedures, immigration, public health, and other

[1] Robert T. Morison, "Search For Ship Automation Solution Starts," *The Journal of Commerce*, New York, December 20, 1963.

[2] Werner Bamberger, "Economy Sought in Ship Subsidies," *The New York Times*, March 2, 1965.

matter relative to arrivals and clearance of vessels, and the treatment of their passengers, crews, cargoes, and baggage.

Attracted by the advantages of faster processing, fewer errors, and less costly paperwork, the Marine Exchange of San Francisco, the Organization of American States (OAS), the United States Government, the Joint Liaison Committee on Documents Used in International Carriage of Goods (JLCD), and other European experts are looking at simplification and standardization of documents and hope to pave the way for an international agreement. The Intergovernmental Maritime Consultative Organization (IMCO) has recently brought together in London some 50 maritime nations for the exchange of views on how documentation can be simplified and what can be done to set up a system on a world-wide basis. It was disclosed that the entrance and clearance of a vessel at a typical port in one country required 28 forms related to the vessel, 22 to the crew, 11 to passengers, and 56 to the cargo—117 forms in all. The conference agreed on a Convention of Facilitation of International Maritime Traffic which will go in effect after ten countries have ratified it. The fact that a uniform document can lend itself to a major application of automated processing equipment provides another big attraction.

As other attempts at international standardization have demonstrated, simplification of ocean-shipping paperwork may require many years of work. Despite the fact that no immediate dramatic results can be anticipated, the direct and indirect gains that would result from standardization fully justify the effort.

TOTAL SYSTEMS APPROACH TO SHIPPING MANAGEMENT

The total systems approach to shipping management, variously called systems, systems engineering, management systems, or management engineering, envisages a planned and well-defined integrated control system of information flow which embraces the entire gamut of company operations. It has the characteristics of a servomechanism device and permits vital information to proceed regularly to the right people at the right time.

The measurement of performance and achievement against targets is essential in the information feedback. This means that there should exist a system that provides for the establishment, collection, processing, and analysis of various operating data. Through the converging or diverging of targets and performance over a period of time, it is possible to assess one's progress and direction. Proper analysis of vessel-voyage data in conjunction with standard cost accounting could very well provide the best foundation for a successful total systems approach in vessel operation.

A typical total systems approach appears below (see *Fairplay Shipping Journal*, London, January 9, 1964, p. 167):

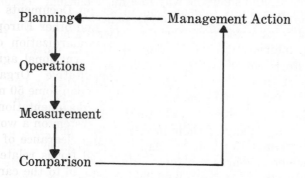

The Role and Potential of Computers and Data Processing

Management decision-making techniques, which until quite recently relied solely on the so-called "experience" and "experimentation" methods, look more and more to the "study and analysis" method for making critical, top-management decisions. This means breaking the problem into its component parts, evaluating the various tangible and intangible factors, and then contemplating the decision in proper perspective. This, in turn, is contingent on the development of more sophisticated and faster-reacting management information systems.

The scientific study of facts and sources takes on a new dimension with the computer because it can now be applied to an extent previously prohibitive in time and costs. Installation of electronic equipment involves rather high initial capital cost, but this outlay is to some extent offset by the potentially low-running cost.

To evaluate performance one is obliged, in almost any business undertaking today, to look at thousands of figures to try to determine whether they convey any information. A simple or multiple regression model can be used to evaluate an entire set of data. A computer can reduce the data to a simple graph or a single list of the figures that differ significantly from the model. It is the ability of the computer to make logical decisions that permits such management-control techniques. Under manual or mechanical systems the method can be uneconomical.

The techniques of the computer age are also making more and more of a mark on transportation. The United States Commerce Department has recently set up a model transportation complex on computers at the University of Pittsburgh. It hopes to learn how to mesh the services of rail, truck, and ship lines, to remove regulatory barriers, and show the way to a more efficient, modern transport system. It will look at containers, piggyback transport, through routes and joint rates, and freight forwarders to find means of improving intermodal coordination of freight movement. Other research efforts conducted by the Commerce Department are probing transportation costs, computerization of tariffs and rate search, and regional transport problems. Airlines, truckers, and railroads are not allowing progress to leave them behind; the electronic brain has been solving many of their problems for some time now.

Computer simulation can be adapted for steamship-management use in continuous short-term forecasting and the associated projection and adjustment of fleet schedules; it is proving a good research tool. Simulation of steamship operations was undertaken in 1958 by Technical Operations, Inc., for the Matson Navigation Company. This was a pioneer effort in the use of computers in steamship operations for tasks other than those of accounting.[3] A more sophisticated computer simulation model has been investigated on behalf of the United States Maritime Administration by a transportation consultant, and described in a paper read before the Society of Naval Architects and Marine Engineers (see Bibliography). Scientists have devised a computer program that can evaluate the characteristics of many types of ships; given all the data, this program can pick the best ship to do the best job under certain conditions. A group of Polish shipbuilders working at the Gdansk Maritime Institute claim to have devised a computer program for preliminary designing calculations of a vessel. A recently formed British company has placed its data-processing know-how, equipment, and a number of useful models at the service of the shipping industry.[4]

All this sounds and *is* very impressive, yet it only scratches the surface of the potential discoveries and benefits. It is the availability of records and data that provides the key to an effective and profitable application of automatic data-processing methods. For

---

[3] Carl A. Friedman, *A Computer Simulation of the Matson Navigation Company's Freighter-Fleet Operations*, Report No. TO-B59-7, April 1959, prepared for Matson Navigation Company by the Technical Operations, Inc., 2 vols.

[4] International Shipping Information Services (ISIS) Limited, 15 Lime Street, London E.C.3, Great Britain.

anyone who contemplates such a move in a year, two, or five, now is the time to begin collecting the various data that one will need. A steamship company can scarcely turn to a computer without a system that collects, analyzes, and presents voyage-operating data in a usable form.

RESEARCH CLEARING HOUSE

A complete separation of the effect of the various items that differentiate ship from ship can produce a meaningful quantitative comparison which may be useful to the shipowner. This, however, would necessitate the analysis of an enormous amount of data beyond the means and capabilities of many operators. It could, however, very easily form the work of some central clearing house to which shipowners would send copies of the abstract logs they receive from their vessels.

This suggestion can be traced to the year 1928.[5] It apparently had no appeal to the shipping community of that generation. Perhaps Mr. Taylor was a visionary, with a concept well ahead of his time. Today we possess the tools in electronic data-processing to make such a project a success. That challenge made 37 years ago can now be realized. Coordination and cooperation are today the key words wherever one turns. Every platform proclaims that the combined ideas of all the maritime interests, so frequently at loggerheads, can be profitably focused to enrich planning, identify possible errors, promote understanding, and allay mistrust. A place that could offer a single roof to ideas, research, differences, and disputes stirs and staggers the imagination. The benefits which would permeate every water-shipping activity would far outweigh the cost of setting up and running such a clearing house.

CLEARING HOUSES NOT NEW

Clearing houses have existed for years in other sectors of the economy. In modern banking and finance their function is deeply rooted. In air transport, the work of a clearing house allows participating airlines to clear accounts with one another regardless of widely varying and complex systems of currency, language, and law. It drastically reduces the need for paperwork, intricate accounting, and large cash settlements. Then there is the biggest model of them all—the United Nations.

---

[5] J. Lockwood Taylor, "Statistical Analysis of Voyage Abstracts," RINA, *Transactions*, 1928, vol. 70, p. 259.

CLEARING HOUSE: PANACEA FOR OTHER PROBLEMS

Internally, most companies circulate a considerable number of reports, forms, and documents designed to record, measure, and facilitate operations. Among steamship companies one may come across reports such as:

Equipment Failure Report	Engineering Trial Record
Tanker Ullage Report	Cargo Tank Gauge Sheets
Boiler Water Report	Corrosion Test Record
Drydocking Report	Subsistence Report
Fuel Abstract	Electrical Log
Hogging and Sagging Calculations	

A project designed to organize and clearly define the function and usefulness of these many reports and forms is long overdue.

A system of documentation that will cover goods from A to Z is just as important to international trade as a transportation system that will carry them. When the elements of a system no longer facilitate the operation, it is time for an overhaul. The documents of international trade are in dire need of an overhaul.

The bill of lading, incidentally, is an excellent source of shipping statistics. It carries such prime information as: shipper, customer, material, weight, route, and the mode of transport. Many firms generate hundreds of bills of lading daily; yet the many statistical benefits are lost because, without the use of computers, data is too costly to retrieve and process.

A systematic review of vessel-entry and vessel-clearance procedures, which in most ports have remained virtually unchanged for a century despite major changes in world conditions, has long been advocated. Present quarantine, immigration, customs, and agricultural requirements often cause ship operators extra (and unnecessary) expense through delays, additional pilotage fees, tug costs, and other incidental services. A review might disclose important areas for improving these practices and eliminating any that might be outmoded.

If the contract documents from the major shipbuilding nations were compared, they would be found to be surprisingly divergent, although their product is essentially similar. Moreover, it is inexplicable that acceptance trials of a vessel worth $7 million or more last only one to three days, while delivery tests for, say, a $1 million paper-making plant takes three or more weeks. It seems hard to justify the lack of detailed description with regard to vessel delivery trials.

At the present time, the various national rules for vessel tonnage measurement produce different figures of vessel net and gross tonnages. The possibility of unifying these rules into an internationally acceptable system of tonnage measurement is being explored by IMCO, but there are no signs, after several years of study, that any great progress has been made so far.

Universal vessel tonnage measurement rules would greatly aid those who seek to organize port statistics in such a way that national and international comparisons could be accomplished. At present, there is no practical and reliable way to measure the output and efficiency of one port against another; there is no standard definition for any of the measures and yardsticks used by ports around the world. Also, for some time now ports have been trying to accommodate an ever-increasing size of vessels in world commerce. Must the ports, at great expense, provide channel depths to satisfy the seemingly unending growth in the size of ships being built, or should some kind of policy be formulated recommending maximum channel depths, a policy tantamount to placing a brake on the development of supertankers and super ore-carriers?

One of the survey respondents pointed out that statistical compilation of certain performance statistics, such as vessel-maintenance figures, on a uniform and industry-wide basis could be of great assistance in ship design and engineering. Certain other operating procedures, such as the maintenance of the "Subsistence Stores Record Book," lend themselves to universal adoption and analysis without any need for individual company identification. The idea of standardized deck and engine logbooks, already explored in these pages, also awaits a standard-bearer.

Unfortunately, these and other interesting suggestions that were brought to light exceed the scope of the present investigation and will not be discussed. All of them, however, merit unqualified support and could very well be considered and evaluated by the proposed maritime research and clearing house.

INTERNATIONAL TRANSPORTATION RESEARCH CLEARING CENTER

Transportation, and all the forms it embraces, must recognize that it is but one element in a total distribution system, and that its role is to perform effectively as part of that system. The manufacturer, who does not render or control transportation services, has been forced to use a segmented service, which by the very nature of being segmented, is more costly and less efficient than if it were a single continuous service from the point of origin to destination like the international postal system (a good example, I might add, only insofar as it exemplifies the "door-to-door" concept and use of integrated transportation). Thus the manufacturer has a big stake in reducing the cost of physical distribution, which is as much a cost to the customer as the cost of manufacture itself. Transportation will, therefore, be most effective when it understands that each industry needs a particular kind of transport service as part of its total distribution program. When a product is made, economists say that "form utility" has been created, which must be accompained by "place utility" by getting the product to the user. "Time utility" follows when the product reaches the user when he needs it. Transportation, being present in all economic activities, must keep pace with the rest of the economy. As a result, today forward-looking transportation men think less about the individual problems of the marine industry, the truckmen, and the rail and air carriers, and more about combinations of these.

Transportation, like politics, because of highly complex international aspects, may be heading toward a "United Nations" forum of its own. Because lip service is being paid to integrated transport and its virtues are extolled only as long as labor is provided protective benefits, integration or coordination per se may turn out to be the most difficult aspect to be resolved in the overall development. Coordinated transportation—a concept which exploits the inherent advantages of each mode of transport—is not encountering a favorable climate, and the road ahead is strewn with obstacles. The existence of an international transportation center would go a long way toward assuring progress and eventual success. A research center, stocked with computers, scientists, and planners to service and set up models for the whole transportation industry, would certainly be in keeping with the demands of the task at hand and our entry into the atomic age.

An international center of this kind could be made responsible for carrying out original research studies in the various forms of transportation. Moreover, it could help all, particularly the less-developed countries of the world to avoid the costly mistakes of the developmental period, and show them the best methods available for solving their transportation problems. Obviously, only the organization of the United Nations, whose geographical framework is truly the world, could provide the necessary stimulus, forum, and leadership to advance and see this proposal through. The organization of the United Nations has its constantly-recurring political difficulties, but its record in the socio-economic field has been salutary and most impressive.

REGIONAL AND NATIONAL TRANSPORTATION CENTERS

However, the need for world-wide cooperation and agreements should not blind us to the fact that there are many issues which can be handled best on a national or regional basis. Often, in our attempts to devise realistic formulas for feasible progress, we tend to play down the piecemeal approach, the gradual build-up toward the final goal.

The Association of American Railroads, for example, has established a new department to handle its own industry-wide problems in the data-processing field, simplify the interchange of data between carriers, and stimulate the development of new railroad data-processing techniques. Also, various agencies using computers and computer techniques in the transportation planning process have formed the Transportation Planning Computer Program Exchange Group. This group discusses and probes a wide field of transportation planning problems and examines how the computer can be used to assist in solving them. The University of Pittsburgh coordinated transportation study for the United States Commerce Department has already been mentioned elsewhere.

The list of similar hopeful signs is growing. What is more important, however, is the fact that the pioneers of the cooperative approach and effort are already with us and can be identified. Unfortunately, the maritime interests have up to now shown little inclination, in spite of some worthwhile attempts, to work together. Successful cooperation and coordination within one's mode of transport at a national or regional level is a prerequisite transition toward the ultimate goal—a world transportation-research center and clearing house.

MARITIME RESEARCH CENTER

The international cyclical swings which have always been a feature of the maritime industry suggest that *international* cooperation is desirable and in the final analysis inevitable. Past attempts by forward-looking men and segments of the industry, often hailed at inception, failed through lack of additional support.

IMCO, the London-based United Nations agency, could serve as a nucleus for such a maritime-resarch clearing house. Most likely, its original purpose may have been just that. Governmental support alone permits this forum to survive, but to prosper it needs a great deal of national or regional backing—of which it presently has very little—from the industry itself. The bulk of the preparatory work for its research, conclusions, and recommendations must be accomplished at the national or regional level. Before IMCO can assume the role of a world maritime transportation center, we need regional subsidiaries of IMCO. North America, South America, Europe, Africa, Asia, and Australasia are the most likely areas where local maritime-research clearing houses could be set up. Most of the shipping world recognizes self-help as an infinitely better alternative to government control or regulation. The minority which holds or is forced to cling to opposite views cannot be excluded on this account from full participation. What is important, however, is keeping political implications to the minimum and not allowing politics to permeate any of the service functions of such a clearing house.

The Maritime Cargo Transportation Conference (MCTC) and the Canadian Bureau of Water Transport might provide the nucleus for a North American maritime center. Inevitably, it would gradually assume many functions now performed by various institutes, societies, conferences, exchanges, and associations. Gradually, the role and importance of the government in general and the Maritime Administration in particular would be greatly curtailed, a development which could hardly be deprecated.

As for the administration of a comparative method for analyzing vessel-voyage data for the whole industry, our proposed clearing house could very well provide the perfect team to see the project through and then stay with it. The impersonality and autonomy of the clearing house, combined with the integrity and impartiality of the staff running it, comprise the essential prerequisites for such a scheme to work. Undoubtedly, the conditions are formidable but not insurmountable. Centralized analysis of vessel-voyage data should not require the shipowner or operator to surrender his identity with his operating data. Only the directly interested operator would get his individual voyage-performance results, which he would then, in the privacy of his office, compare to national or international averages for different classes of vessels in operation. Since most of the work that a clearing house would perform would come under the category of providing a service (centralized R&D function), there is no reason why it could not become self-supporting after an initial period of operating as a marginal undertaking in need of assistance. The self-supporting concept is the best guarantee of autonomy and impartiality.

SUMMARY AND CONCLUSIONS

Research and its resultant new concepts appear to be the thin end of the wedge that is opening new horizons for all modes of transportation. Promising innovations and experiments have managed to disturb even the complacency of ocean shipping men.

Obviously, the short discourse on the proposed research clearing house for transportation can only be offered as a basis for discussion, inviting counterproposals, then final compromises. The drawbacks, it would seem, can be corrected without discarding the general structure of the plan.

CHAPTER VII

Conclusion

Progress is achieved through man's search for new and better ways to do things. While he forges ahead, man also needs to pause occasionally to review the results of what he has done and where he is going. Systematic analysis of vessel-voyage data can uncover opportunities for improvement; it is absolutely essential for dynamic operations.

In many fields of human endeavor the comparative approach has opened new horizons and a broader understanding of complex processes. We have the tools and methods for diverse kinds of analyses, but there is chaos and confusion in our methods of collecting and presenting data and facts. The comparative method for collecting and analyzing vessel-voyage data explored in these pages was not designed to provide a terminal appraisal, but rather a starting point and a framework.

In this volume we have traced the evolution of voyage-data analysis to its current status. Because of the dearth of material on the subject, a survey was conducted which readily disclosed that consistent recording and analyzing of voyage data has not become, with some notable exceptions, a matter of standard practice. It further disclosed willingness and readiness among the majority of steamship operators to consider an acceptable universal method of voyage-data analysis.

Two chapters have been dedicated to exploring the formulation of a uniform comparative method embracing a set of appropriate standardized forms for analyzing voyage results, and then exposing the value of these forms to a test of practical application.

After expounding on some of the economic and practical aspects of analyzing voyage data, determining standards that represent a desired performance, and evaluating that performance, we have looked at the new and exciting transportation concepts and the role of research. It was shown that the current drive and desire to automate planning and decision-making functions makes research absolutely necessary both as a ground-breaking and a supplementary feature. Transportation research, as all research, requires the use of a heterogeneous mass of changing data. Computers, automatic data-processing, operations research, program evaluation and review technique (PERT), input-output models, etc., call for the institution of new and special data-collection techniques to feed the expanding research activities. This volume suggests large areas that would be productive in projects that are susceptible to programming and solution by means of the computer.

The economic demands of the period we are now entering are gradually but surely relegating shipping to the role of being but one element in a total distribution system. The ship and port will diminish slowly as focal points of international commerce and business activity to become, like other modes of transport, merely a link in a system of transportation. The minimum economical cargo flow required by highly mechanized terminals is likely to produce a very distinct trend toward minimizing the number of transfer points and increasing the size and speed of carriers. This, in turn, will create standard conditions that will require the application of standardized methods. All of the far-reaching changes and developments that are taking place in cargo-handling, ship design and construction, and automation make vessel-voyage-data collection and analysis an indispensable ingredient in progress. The "clearing house" idea has the best chance of coming up with the right models and guidelines by placing centralized research and concentrating forward-thinking under one roof.

The specialized bulk-carrier and the container vessel serving only the major and most generally utilized routes of traffic are best suited to fill the role of the ocean carrier in the new transportation concept. The need for optimum utilization and economical operation clearly calls for the use of a uniform vessel-voyage-data collection and analysis system. The standardized comparative method for analyzing voyage results, as described in these pages, may, it is hoped, fill the need for this kind of an operational and managerial tool. The changing transportation concepts not only emphasize the value of this control tool, but also facilitate its introduction and profitable application.

Appendix

APPENDIX A

Kim J. Loroch,
104-60 Queens Blvd.
Forest Hills, N.Y., 11375 USA

Gentlemen:

Re: "Comparative Method for Analyzing Vessel Voyage Data
Including Performance Standards and Ratings"

I am currently engaged in writing a thesis in the area of foreign trade for a Master's degree (M.B.A.) at the City College of New York. Essentially, my thesis will revolve around a system I have devised and put into practice for analyzing vessel voyage data carried by deck and engine logbooks. A somewhat chaotic situation appears to exist and there seem to be as many systems intended for this purpose as the number of shipping organizations. My aim is to establish the need for a standardized method which can be used by any company operating one or hundreds of vessels in one or many trades. In line with the general trend such a simple and flexible arrangement offering standard forms and a uniform approach may prove to be economically desirable. Moreover, it may disclose valuable operational, planning, and policy-making aspects.

The writer has served the shipping industry at sea and ashore for many years in various capacities that embrace management, operation, chartering, and research. Present duties, as staff member of the Port of New York Authority's Port Development Department, center around marine planning and research.

In order to make my study meaningful and to show its relation to currently prevailing arrangements, I am trying to reach a representative cross section of the shipping industry by means of the attached questionnaire. Various institutions and associations will find some of the questions inapplicable since the questionnaire has been designed primarily for steamship operating companies. Since the progress of my thesis is linked to a timetable set up by the College, the return of the questionnaire to the above address within four weeks is essential.

After the thesis is accepted and if found worthwhile, I will seek ways to make it available to the shipping industry.

Yours sincerely,

Kim J. Loroch

Enc

QUESTIONNAIRE

"COMPARATIVE METHOD FOR ANALYZING VESSEL VOYAGE DATA INCLUDING PERFORMANCE STANDARDS AND RATINGS"

Name of Organization _____

Address _____

Name and Title of Person _____

1. What department in your organization is responsible for collecting, analyzing and presenting vessel voyage data? _____

2. Do you methodically and systematically analyze such data? Please outline main features of your system. _____
   _____
   _____

3. Apart from log books what other documents or forms do you employ for data collection? _____

4. What is the approximate time consumed between the end of a voyage and the receipt of all necessary documents and forms for analyzing that voyage? _____

5. Does your system of analysis include a comparison of various vessel operating data on a ship and fleet basis? _____

6. What statistical tools are used to achieve the comparison? _____
   _____

7. Are performance standards and/or ratings included in your system of analysis? ____

8. Please define basis for calculation of performance standards and/or ratings in use.
   _____
   _____

9. If you were given the means and opportunity to reorganize or improve your system indicate and outline areas of importance and suggested changes. _____
   _____
   _____

10. What other departments within the organization utilize your voyage data presentation and analysis? _____

11. Do you feel there is a need within the shipping industry for a universal system that would offer standard forms, uniform approach, effective controls, and comparative analysis and presentation of vessel voyage data? _____
    _____

12. Would you give serious consideration towards adopting such a system? _____

13. Since my research indicates that very little has been written on this subject, your help in locating pertinent literature would be very much appreciated. _____
    _____

14. For any additional comments of value to this study please use the other side or attach additional pages. _____

15. Please indicate if the name of your organization may be used in this study. Yes__No__

Please return to: Kim J. Loroch,
104-60 Queens Blvd.
Forest Hills, N.Y. 11375 USA

APPENDIX B: AUXILIARY TABLES

TABLE B-1

DECIMAL PARTS OF AN HOUR FOR EACH MINUTE

1	.01667	16	.26667	31	.51667	46	.76667
2	.03333	17	.28333	32	.53333	47	.78333
3	.05000	18	.30000	33	.55000	48	.80000
4	.06667	19	.31667	34	.56667	49	.81667
5	.08333	20	.33333	35	.58333	50	.83333
6	.10000	21	.25000	36	.60000	51	.85000
7	.11667	22	.36667	37	.61667	52	.86667
8	.13333	23	.38333	38	.63333	53	.88333
9	.15000	24	.40000	39	.65000	54	.90000
10	.16667	25	.41667	40	.66667	55	.91667
11	.18333	26	.43333	41	.68333	56	.93333
12	.20000	27	.45000	42	.70000	57	.95000
13	.21667	28	.46667	43	.71667	58	.96667
14	.23333	29	.48333	44	.73333	59	.98333
15	.25000	30	.50000	45	.75000	60	1.00000

Note. A useful table for converting minutes into decimal parts of an hour. Example: 2 hours 46 minutes = 2.76667 hours.

TABLE B-2

CUMULATIVE HOURS FOR THIRTY DAYS

1	24	7	168	13	312	19	456	25	600
2	48	8	192	14	336	20	480	26	624
3	72	9	216	15	360	21	504	27	648
4	96	10	240	16	384	22	528	28	672
5	120	11	264	17	408	23	552	29	696
6	144	12	288	18	432	24	576	30	720

TABLE B-3

DECIMAL PARTS OF A DAY

Minutes	Hours 0	1	2	3	4	5	6	7	8	9	10	11
1	0007	0424	0840	1256	1673	2090	2506	2923	3340	3756	4173	4589
2	14	31	47	63	80	97	13	30	47	63	80	96
3	21	37	54	70	87	2104	20	37	54	70	87	4603
4	28	44	61	77	94	11	27	44	61	77	94	10
5	35	51	68	84	1701	18	34	51	68	84	4201	17
6	42	58	75	91	08	24	41	58	75	91	07	24
7	49	65	82	98	15	31	48	65	82	98	14	31
8	56	72	89	1305	22	38	55	72	89	3805	21	38
9	62	79	96	12	29	45	62	79	95	12	28	45
10	69	86	0903	19	36	52	69	86	3402	19	35	52
11	76	93	10	26	43	59	76	93	09	26	42	58
12	83	0500	17	33	49	66	83	99	16	33	49	65
13	90	07	24	40	56	73	90	3006	23	40	56	72
14	97	14	31	47	63	80	97	13	30	47	63	79
15	0104	21	38	54	70	87	2604	20	37	54	70	86
16	11	28	44	61	77	94	11	27	44	61	77	93
17	18	35	51	68	84	2201	18	34	51	68	84	4700
18	25	42	58	74	91	08	24	41	58	74	91	07
19	32	49	65	81	98	15	31	48	65	81	98	14
20	39	56	72	88	1805	22	38	55	72	88	4305	21
21	46	62	79	95	12	29	45	62	79	95	12	28
22	53	69	86	1402	19	36	52	69	86	3902	19	35
23	60	76	93	09	26	43	59	76	93	09	26	42
24	67	83	1000	16	33	49	66	83	99	16	32	49
25	75	90	07	23	40	56	73	90	3506	23	39	55
26	81	97	13	30	47	63	80	97	13	30	46	62
27	87	0604	20	37	54	70	87	3104	20	37	53	69
28	94	11	28	44	61	77	94	11	27	44	60	76
29	0201	18	35	51	68	84	2701	18	34	51	67	83
30	08	25	42	58	74	91	08	24	41	58	74	90
31	15	32	49	65	81	98	15	31	48	64	81	97
32	22	39	55	72	88	2305	22	38	55	71	88	4804
33	29	46	62	79	95	12	29	45	62	78	95	11
34	36	53	69	86	1902	19	36	52	69	85	4402	18
35	43	60	76	93	09	26	43	59	76	92	09	25
36	50	67	83	99	16	33	49	66	83	99	16	32
37	57	74	90	1506	23	40	56	73	90	4006	23	39
38	63	81	97	13	30	47	63	80	97	13	30	46
39	70	88	1104	20	37	54	71	87	3604	20	37	53
40	78	94	11	27	44	61	78	94	11	27	44	60
41	85	0701	18	34	51	68	84	3201	18	34	51	67
42	92	08	25	41	58	74	91	08	24	41	57	74
43	99	15	32	48	65	81	98	15	31	48	64	80
44	0306	22	39	55	72	88	2805	22	38	55	71	87
45	12	29	46	62	79	95	12	29	45	62	78	94
46	19	36	53	69	86	2402	19	36	52	69	85	4901
47	26	43	60	76	93	09	26	43	59	76	92	08
48	33	50	67	83	99	16	33	50	66	83	99	15
49	40	57	74	90	2006	23	40	57	73	90	4506	22
50	47	64	81	97	13	30	47	64	80	96	13	29
51	54	71	87	1604	20	37	54	71	87	4103	20	36
52	61	78	94	11	27	44	61	77	94	10	27	43
53	68	85	1201	18	34	51	68	84	3701	17	34	50
54	75	92	08	25	41	58	74	91	08	24	41	57
55	82	99	15	31	48	65	81	98	15	31	48	64
56	89	0806	22	38	55	72	88	3305	22	38	55	71
57	96	12	29	45	62	79	95	12	29	45	62	78
58	0403	19	36	52	69	86	2902	19	36	52	68	85
59	10	26	43	59	76	93	09	26	43	59	75	92
60	17	33	50	66	83	2500	16	33	50	66	82	5000

Note. A useful table for converting hours and minutes into decimal

FOR EACH HOUR AND MINUTE

Hours

12	13	14	15	16	17	18	19	20	21	22	23		Minutes
5006	5423	5840	6256	6673	7090	7507	7923	8340	8756	9173	9590		1
13	30	47	63	80	97	13	30	47	63	80	97		2
20	37	54	70	87	7105	20	37	54	70	87	9604		3
27	44	61	77	94	12	27	44	61	77	94	11		4
34	51	68	84	6701	18	34	51	68	84	9201	18		5
41	58	74	91	08	25	41	58	74	91	08	24		6
48	65	81	98	15	31	48	65	81	98	15	31		7
55	72	88	6305	22	38	55	72	88	8805	22	38		8
62	79	95	12	29	45	62	79	95	12	29	45		9
69	86	5902	19	36	52	69	86	8402	19	36	52		10
76	93	09	26	43	59	76	93	09	26	43	59		11
83	99	16	33	49	66	83	99	16	33	49	66		12
90	5506	23	40	56	73	90	8006	23	40	56	73		13
97	13	30	47	63	80	97	13	30	47	63	80		14
5104	20	37	54	70	87	7604	20	37	54	70	87		15
11	27	44	61	77	94	11	27	44	61	77	94		16
18	34	51	68	84	7201	18	34	51	68	84	9701		17
24	41	58	74	91	08	24	41	58	74	91	08		18
31	48	65	81	98	15	31	48	65	81	98	15		19
38	55	72	88	6805	22	38	55	72	88	9305	22		20
45	62	79	95	12	29	45	62	79	96	12	29		21
52	69	86	6402	19	36	52	69	86	8903	19	36		22
59	76	93	09	26	43	59	76	93	09	26	43		23
66	83	99	16	33	49	66	83	99	16	33	50		24
73	90	6006	23	40	56	73	90	8506	23	40	56		25
80	97	13	30	47	63	80	97	13	30	47	63		26
87	5604	20	37	54	70	87	8104	20	37	54	70		27
94	11	27	44	61	77	94	11	27	44	61	77		28
5201	18	34	51	68	84	7701	18	34	51	68	84		29
08	24	41	58	74	91	08	24	41	58	74	91		30
15	31	48	65	81	98	15	31	48	65	81	98		31
22	38	55	72	88	7305	22	38	55	72	88	9805		32
29	45	62	79	95	12	29	45	62	79	95	12		33
36	52	69	86	6902	19	36	52	69	86	9402	19		34
43	59	76	93	09	26	43	59	76	93	09	26		35
49	66	83	99	16	33	49	66	83	99	16	33		36
56	73	90	6506	23	40	56	73	90	9006	23	40		37
63	80	97	13	30	47	63	80	97	13	30	47		38
70	87	6104	20	37	54	70	87	8604	20	37	52		39
77	94	11	27	44	61	77	94	11	27	44	61		40
84	5701	18	34	51	68	84	8201	18	34	51	68		41
91	08	24	41	58	75	91	08	25	41	58	74		42
98	15	31	48	65	81	98	15	31	48	65	81		43
5305	22	38	55	72	88	7805	22	38	55	72	88		44
12	29	45	62	79	95	12	29	45	62	79	95		45
19	36	52	69	86	7402	19	36	52	68	86	9902		46
26	43	59	76	93	09	26	43	59	75	93	09		47
33	49	66	83	7000	16	33	50	66	82	9500	16		48
40	56	73	90	07	23	40	57	73	89	06	23		49
47	63	80	97	13	30	47	63	80	96	13	30		50
54	70	87	6604	20	37	54	70	87	9103	20	37		51
61	77	94	11	27	44	61	77	94	10	27	44		52
68	84	6201	18	34	51	68	84	8701	17	34	51		53
74	91	08	25	41	58	75	91	08	24	41	58		54
81	98	15	31	48	65	81	98	15	31	48	65		55
88	5805	22	38	55	72	88	8305	22	38	55	72		56
95	12	29	45	62	79	95	12	29	45	62	79		57
5402	19	36	52	69	86	7902	19	36	52	69	86		58
09	26	43	59	76	93	09	26	43	59	76	93		59
16	33	50	66	83	7500	16	33	50	66	83	10000		60

parts of a day. Example: 2 days 16 hours 32 minutes = 2.6888 days.

TABLE B-4

WEIGHT OF FUEL OIL IN POUNDS PER BARREL (42 GALLONS)

API	.0	.1	.2	.3	.4	.5	.6	.7	.8	.9
2	370.8	370.5	370.2	369.9	369.6	369.4	369.1	368.8	368.5	368.3
3	368.0	367.7	367.4	367.2	366.9	366.6	366.3	366.1	365.8	365.5
4	365.3	365.0	364.7	364.5	364.2	363.9	363.7	363.4	363.1	362.9
5	362.6	362.3	362.1	361.8	361.5	361.3	361.0	360.7	360.5	360.2
6	360.0	359.7	359.4	359.2	358.9	358.6	358.4	358.1	357.9	357.6
7	357.4	357.1	356.8	356.6	356.3	356.1	355.8	355.6	355.3	355.0
8	354.8	354.5	354.3	354.0	353.8	353.5	353.3	353.0	352.8	352.5
9	352.3	352.0	351.8	351.5	351.3	351.0	350.8	350.5	350.3	350.0
10	349.8	349.5	349.3	349.0	348.8	348.5	348.3	348.1	347.8	347.6
11	347.3	347.1	346.8	346.6	346.3	346.1	345.9	345.6	345.4	345.1
12	344.9	344.7	344.4	344.2	343.9	343.7	343.5	343.2	343.0	342.8
13	342.5	342.3	342.0	341.8	341.6	341.3	341.1	340.9	340.6	340.4
14	340.1	339.9	339.7	339.5	339.2	339.0	338.8	338.5	338.3	338.1
15	337.8	337.6	337.4	337.2	336.9	336.7	336.5	336.2	336.0	335.8
16	335.5	335.3	335.1	334.9	334.6	334.4	334.2	334.0	333.7	333.5
17	333.3	333.1	332.8	332.6	332.4	332.2	332.0	331.7	331.5	331.3
18	331.1	330.8	330.6	330.4	330.2	330.0	329.7	329.5	329.3	329.1
19	328.9	328.6	328.4	328.2	328.0	327.8	327.6	327.3	327.1	326.9
20	326.7	326.5	326.3	326.0	325.8	325.6	325.4	325.2	325.0	324.8
21	324.5	324.3	324.1	323.9	323.7	323.5	323.3	323.1	322.9	322.6
22	322.4	322.2	322.0	321.8	321.6	321.4	321.2	321.0	320.8	320.6
23	320.3	320.1	319.9	319.7	319.5	319.3	319.1	318.9	318.7	318.5
24	318.3	318.1	317.9	317.7	317.5	317.3	317.1	316.9	316.7	316.5
25	316.3	316.1	315.8	315.6	315.4	315.2	315.0	314.8	314.6	314.4
26	314.2	314.0	313.8	313.7	313.5	313.3	313.1	312.9	312.7	312.5
27	312.3	312.1	311.9	311.7	311.5	311.3	311.1	310.9	310.7	310.5
28	310.3	310.1	309.9	309.7	309.5	309.3	309.1	309.0	308.8	308.6
29	308.4	308.2	308.0	307.8	307.6	307.4	307.2	307.0	306.8	306.7
30	306.5	306.3	306.1	305.9	305.7	305.5	305.3	305.1	305.0	304.8
31	304.6	304.4	304.2	304.0	303.8	303.6	303.5	303.3	303.1	302.9
32	302.7	302.5	302.3	302.2	302.0	301.8	301.6	301.4	301.2	301.1
33	300.9	300.7	300.5	300.3	300.1	300.0	299.8	299.6	299.4	299.2
34	299.1	298.9	298.7	298.5	298.3	298.2	298.0	297.8	297.6	297.4

Compiled from Tagliabue Formula - S. G. = $\frac{141.5}{131.5 - A.P.I.}$

2° - 10° A.P.I. Confirmed by Oil & Gas Journal 5/17/28
A.S.T.M. Committee D-2   May 23, 1928

Note. The oil industry determines and expresses specific gravity of oil in degrees on the American Petroleum Institute (API) scale. This scale fixes a reading of 10 degrees as equal to a specific gravity of 1.00. Readings above 10 degrees indicate specific gravity less than 1.00 or an oil lighter than water. Specific gravities are used in computing the weights of unit volumes, since oils are commonly sold either by the volume in gallons or barrels of 42 gallons. The table shows the weight in pounds per barrel of oil in accordance with its assigned API degrees; e.g., a barrel of oil with 25.6 API degrees weighs 315 pounds.

TABLE B-5

TABLE OF DAYS BETWEEN TWO DATES

Day	January	February	March	April	May	June	July	August	September	October	November	December
1	1	32	60	91	121	152	182	213	244	274	305	335
2	2	33	61	92	122	153	183	214	245	275	306	336
3	3	34	62	93	123	154	184	215	246	276	307	337
4	4	35	63	94	124	155	185	216	247	277	308	338
5	5	36	64	95	125	156	186	217	248	278	309	339
6	6	37	65	96	126	157	187	218	249	279	310	340
7	7	38	66	97	127	158	188	219	250	280	311	341
8	8	39	67	98	128	159	189	220	251	281	312	342
9	9	40	68	99	129	160	190	221	252	282	313	343
10	10	41	69	100	130	161	191	222	253	283	314	344
11	11	42	70	101	131	162	192	223	254	284	315	345
12	12	43	71	102	132	163	193	224	255	285	316	346
13	13	44	72	103	133	164	194	225	256	286	317	347
14	14	45	73	104	134	165	195	226	257	287	318	348
15	15	46	74	105	135	166	196	227	258	288	319	349
16	16	47	75	106	136	167	197	228	259	289	320	350
17	17	48	76	107	137	168	198	229	260	290	321	351
18	18	49	77	108	138	169	199	230	261	291	322	352
19	19	50	78	109	139	170	200	231	262	292	323	353
20	20	51	79	110	140	171	201	232	263	293	324	354
21	21	52	80	111	141	172	202	233	264	294	325	355
22	22	53	81	112	142	173	203	234	265	295	326	356
23	23	54	82	113	143	174	204	235	266	296	327	357
24	24	55	83	114	144	175	205	236	267	297	328	358
25	25	56	84	115	145	176	206	237	268	298	329	359
26	26	57	85	116	146	177	207	238	269	299	330	360
27	27	58	86	117	147	178	208	239	270	300	331	361
28	28	59	87	118	148	179	209	240	271	301	332	362
29	29	..	88	119	149	180	210	241	272	302	333	363
30	30	..	89	120	150	181	211	242	273	303	334	364
31	31	..	90	...	151	...	212	243	...	304	...	365

For leap year, one day must be added to each number of days after Feb. 28.

Note. This is a useful table for quick determination of the number of days between any two dates within a year. Example: January 1 to July 19 = 200 days. February 19 to September 7 = -50 days + 250 days = 200 days.

TABLE B-6

SPEED, TIME, AND DISTANCE TABLE

Nautical Miles Covered in Relation to Ship's Speed and Sailing Days

TABLE B-7

GENERAL SHIP CHARACTERISTICS

	Liberty EC-2	Victory VC-2	C-1 Cargo	C-2 Cargo	C-3 Cargo	T-2 Tanker	Mariner CA-S-12
G.R.T. (U.S.)	7176	7607	6724	6214	7974	10448	9216
N.R.T. (U.S.)	4380	4561	3953	3508	4619	6870	5366
Length overall	441'6"	455'3"	417'9"	459'6"	492'0"	523'6"	563'8"
Breadth molded	57'0"	62'1-5/8"	60'0"	63'0"	69'6"	68'0"	76'0"
Grainspace	530307	523740	505877	601564	694207	-	837305
Balespace	475043	453210	451624	529984	629526	15203	736723
Reeferspace	-	-	-	-	-	-	30254
Fuel – Bbls.	12059	19113	12729	11219	20919	9735	25250
Fuel – Tons	1827	2882	1920	1710	3045	1470	3808
Water – Tons	450	435	343	581	540	365	257
Stores	150	150	150	150	150	150	150
Freeboard – Summer	9'8-3/4"	9'7"	10'3"	13'6"	4'6-1/4"	7'8"	5'9-1/2"
Freeboard – Winter	10'3-3/4"	10'2"	10'10"	14'1"	5'1-1/4"	8'3"	6'5"
Freeboard – Tropical	9'1-3/4"	9'0"	9'8"	12'11"	3'11-1/4"	7'1"	5'2"
Draft – Summer	27'9-1/4"	28'6-3/4"	27'7-3/4"	27'0"	29'1"	30'0-1/4"	29'10-1/16"
Draft – Winter	27'2-1/4"	27'11-3/4"	27'0-3/4"	26'5"	28'6"	29'5-1/4"	29'2-9/16"
Draft – Tropical	28'4-1/4"	29'1-3/4"	28'2-3/4"	27'7"	29'8"	30'7-1/4"	30'5-9/16"
Deadweight – Summer	10920	10717	8753	10100	12030	16613	13418
Deadweight – Winter	10569	10357	8452	9753	11610	16165	12878
Deadweight – Tropical	11261	11077	9054	10447	12450	17061	13958
Displacement – Summer	14257	15199	12875	14600	17980	21722	21093
Displacement – Winter	13906	14830	12574	14253	17560	21274	20553
Displacement – Tropical	14598	15559	13176	14947	18400	22170	21633
Light Ship	3337	4481	4122	5400	5950	5109	7675
Speed	10	15	14.5	15	16	14.5	20
Engine Output (SHP)	2500(IHP)	6000	4150	6000	8500	6000	17500
Bbls. per mile	0.630	0.680	0.600	0.650	0.720	0.780	1.030
Capacity – Bbls.	-	-	-	-	-	1141158	-

Note: All figures are approximate and subject to change for any particular vessel.

CONVERSION TABLE – UNITS OF MEASURE

TO OBTAIN — MULTIPLY BY

KNOWING — Volume Measure (liquid)	U.S. GALLON	U.S. BARREL (42 gals)	IMPERIAL GALLON	CUBIC FEET	LITRES	HECTOLITRES
U.S. Gallon	-	0.0238	0.8327	0.1336	3.7853	0.0379
U.S. Barrel (42 gals)	42.0	-	35.0	5.6112	158.98	1.5898
Imperial Gallon	1.203	0.0286	-	0.1603	4.546	0.0455
Cubic Feet	7.4805	0.1782	6.2289	-	28.316	0.2832
Litres	0.2642	0.0063	0.2199	0.0353	-	0.01
Hectolitres	26.418	0.63	21.998	3.5315	100.0	-

Weight Measure	POUNDS	SHORT TONS (2000 lbs)	LONG TONS (2240 lbs)	KILOGRAMS	METRIC TONS
Pounds	-	0.0005	0.00045	0.4536	0.00045
Short Tons (2000 lbs)	2000.0	-	0.8929	907.2	0.9072
Long Tons (2240 lbs)	2240.0	1.120	-	1016.0	1.016
Kilograms	2.205	0.0011	0.00098	-	0.001
Metric Tons	2205.0	1.102	0.9842	1000.0	-

Linear Measure (small)	YARDS	FEET	INCHES	METRES	DECIMETRES	CENTIMETRES
Yards	-	3.0	36.0	0.9144	9.144	91.44
Feet	0.3333	-	12.0	0.3048	3.048	30.48
Inches	0.0277	0.0833	-	0.0254	0.254	2.540
Metres	1.094	3.281	39.37	-	10.0	100.0
Decimetres	0.1094	0.3281	3.937	0.1	-	10.0
Centimetres	0.0109	0.0328	0.3937	0.01	0.1	-

Linear Measure (large)	NAUTICAL MILES	LAND MILES	YARDS	FEET	KILOMETRES	METRES
Nautical Miles	-	1.152	2027.0	6080.0	1.853	1853.0
Land Miles	0.8684	-	1760.0	5280.0	1.609	1609.0
Yards	0.0005	0.0006	-	3.0	0.0009	0.9144
Feet	0.0002	0.0002	0.3333	-	0.0003	0.3048
Kilometres	0.5396	0.6214	1094.0	3281.0	-	1000.0
Metres	0.0005	0.0006	1.094	3.281	0.0001	-

Displacement. Vessel displaces its own weight of water. Cubic measurement of vessel's underwater portion multiplied by 64 then divided by 35 gives weight (tons of 2240 lbs) of salt water displaced, or vessel's weight.

Light Displacement. Vessel's weight (tons of 2240 lbs) less cargo, passengers, fuel, stores, water, dunnage, and such other items necessary for use on a voyage.

Loaded Displacement. Vessel's weight (tons of 2240 lbs) down to her marks, including cargo, passengers, fuel, stores, water, dunnage, and such other items necessary for use on a voyage.

Deadweight. Vessel's carrying capacity (tons of 2240 lbs) i.e., the difference between loaded and light displacements.

Cargo Deadweight. Vessel's remaining carrying capacity (tons of 2240 lbs) after deducting from deadweight tonnage fuel, water, stores, dunnage, and such other items necessary for use on a voyage.

Gross. Vessel's entire internal cubic capacity (volume) of all closed-in spaces less certain exemptions (1 gross ton = 100 cubic feet).

Net. Vessel's remaining internal cubic capacity (volume) after deducting certain exempt spaces from gross tonnage (1 net ton = 100 cubic feet).

Register. Applicable to both gross and net tonnages (usually the latter). Shown on vessel's national documents of registration, hence the name.

Suez & Panama. Vessel's internal cubic capacity (volume); as a rule larger than register tonnage because of fewer allowed space exemptions. (1 ton = 100 cubic feet).

Underdeck. Vessel's internal cubic space (volume) between the top of ceiling or double bottom in the hold and the under surface of tonnage deck (1 ton = 100 cubic feet).

Tweendeck. Vessel's internal cubic space (volume) between tonnage deck and upper deck (1 ton = 100 cubic feet).

Power. Gross tonnage added to indicated horsepower (IHP) classifies a vessel for establishing officers' rates of pay.

Equipment. Vessel's internal cubic space (volume) under freeboard deck (1 ton = 100 cubic feet) and in the second tier of superstructure (1 ton = 200 cubic feet) determines weights and sizes of anchors, and other equipment.

Related Terms

Grain Cubic. Maximum cargo space (cubic feet) measured to outside of frames, to top of ceiling, and to top of beams, including hatchways.

Bale Cubic. Cargo space (cubic feet) measured to inside of cargo battens, to top of ceiling, and to underside of beams, including hatchways.

Stowage Factor. Bale (or grain) cubic capacity divided by cargo deadweight. Also number of cubic feet actually occupied by one ton (2240 lbs.) of a commodity.

Tonnage Deck. The uppermost deck in single- or double-deck vessels and the second continuous deck from the keel in all other vessels.

Freeboard. Vertical distance from freeboard deck (uppermost continuous deck) to the loadlines indicating maximum permissible draught measured amidships.

Broken Stowage. Cargo space unavoidably lost when stowing general cargo.

Marks (Freeboard). Assigned waterline height to which a vessel may be loaded.

APPENDIX C: NOTES ON HORSEPOWER CALCULATION

The steam reciprocating engine has largely been replaced by Diesel engines and steam turbine propulsion in merchant vessels.

The capacity of an engine is usually measured in horsepower (one HP = 33,000 foot-pounds per minute). The power within the cylinder or cylinders of an engine is referred to as the indicated horsepower (IHP). Because of friction, windage, and other mechanical losses, the power that may be applied to useful purposes is always less than the indicated horsepower and is known as brake horsepower (BHP). The ratio of brake horsepower to indicated horsepower (BHP/IHP) represents an indicator of mechanical efficiency. Depending on the design and workmanship, the mechanical efficiencies of steam engines at normal loads range from 85 to 95 per cent. The torsion of a shaft which transmits the power affects the friction in the collar, the journal bearing, and the propeller lining, resulting in the shaft horsepower (SHP) being somewhat lower than the braking capacity (BHP).

One of several methods of measuring shaft horsepower is by means of a torsionmeter. Under full power conditions, an accuracy within ± 2 per cent can be expected. A number of vessels have also been fitted with a thrustmeter which permits an analysis of the propeller efficiency and the required thrust to maintain a given speed. The torsionmeter should be considered standard equipment by shipbuilders and ship operators. Although fairly common in European vessels, very few United States vessels carry torsionmeters for determining shaft horsepower, making it necessary for power to be estimated by one of several crude methods. Of course, meters to measure torque, power and flow of fuel form an integral part of efficiency monitoring systems which, in turn, are part of shipboard automation.

In the case of turbine power plants, the shaft horsepower (SHP) may be determined with the help of the turbine manufacturer's set of engine power curves and the engine-room watch operational data found in the engine logbook and most abstracts. The number of nozzle valves in use and the observed high-pressure-turbine chest pressure determines the uncorrected shaft horsepower (SHP), which is then corrected for changes in propeller speed, turbine temperatures, and condenser vacuum as in the following example:

TABLE C-1

SHAFT HORSEPOWER CALCULATION

Operational Data	From Engine Log Book or Abstract	From Turbine Manufacturer's Power Curves
SHP (uncorrected)	-	13,900
No. of Nozzle Valves Open	6	-
H. P. Chest Pressure (psig)	1450	-
H. P. Chest Temperature (°F)	740	0.0%
I. P. Inlet Temperature (°F)	555	-0.3%
L. P. Inlet Temperature (°F)	540	-1.0%
Vacuum Main Condenser (Hq)	27.65	-2.9%
RPM (daily/passage average)	94.50	+0.4%
Total Percentage Correction	-	-3.8%
SHP (corrected)	-	13,372

The indicated horsepower (IHP) of Diesel engines may be calculated from the following equation,[1] provided an indicator can be used and the diagrams are reasonably accurate:

$$IHP = \frac{Pm\ L\ A\ N'}{33,000}$$

where

Pm = mean effective pressure, psi
L = length of stroke, ft.
A = cross-sectional area of cylinder, sq. in.
N' = number of explosions per minute

The power produced within the ends of a double-acting steam cylinder is expressed as:[2]

$$IHP\ (head\text{-}end) = \frac{Pm\ L\ A\ N}{33,000}$$

$$IHP\ (crank\text{-}end) = \frac{P'm\ L\ A'\ N}{33,000}$$

where

Pm = head-end mean effective pressure, psi
$P'm$ = crank-end mean effective pressure, psi
L = length of engine stroke, ft.
A = net piston area, head-end, sq. in.
A' = net piston area, crank-end, sq. in.
N = revolutions per minute

The quantities LA/33,000 and LA'/33,000 are always fixed for an engine. These ratios are known respectively as head-end and crank-end engine constants.

The indicator, when properly attached to a cylinder, draws a curve whose base line represents the travel of the piston and whose ordinate (perpendicular distance from a straight line to a point in a curve) shows the pressure at each moment of the travel. A mechanical device, known as a polar planimeter, is used for measuring the work area of an indicator diagram. Knowing the area of the diagram, the mean height or mean ordinate (O) may be determined by dividing the diagram in square inches by the extreme length in inches of the enclosed area. The mean effective pressure (Pm) within the engine cylinder is equal to the product of the mean ordinate (O) of the indicator diagram and the given indicator spring constant (S) expressed in pounds per square inch, that is, Pm = O × S. The total indicated horsepower (IHP) of the multi-cylinder engine is the sum of the horsepowers developed in the individual cylinders.

The direct-acting, condensing, three-cylinder, triple-expansion, steam-reciprocating power plant of a Liberty Vessel (EC2-S-C1) is designed to develop 2500 IHP at 76 rpm. The following step-by-step example uses actual operating data and diagrams supplied by such a vessel upon completion of a voyage.

---

[1] William H. Severns and Howard E. Degler, *Steam, Air and Gas Power*, 4th Edition, John Wiley & Sons, Inc., New York, 1948, p. 466.

[2] *Ibid.*, pp. 264-268.

TABLE C-2
INDICATED HORSEPOWER CALCULATION

LIBERTY VESSEL - EC2-S-C1 -		HIGH PRESSURE CYLINDER - HP -	INTERMEDIATE PRESSURE CYLINDER - IP -	LOW PRESSURE CYLINDER - LP -
Diameter	In.	24.5	37.0	70.0
Net Piston Area				
Head-End (A)	Sq. In.	471.436	1075.213	3848.460
Crank-End (A')	Sq. In.	432.951	1036.728	3809.975
Engine Stroke Length (L)	Ft.	4.0	4.0	4.0
ENGINE CONSTANTS:				
Head-End (C) = $\frac{L \times A}{33,000}$		$\frac{4 \times 471.436}{33,000} = 0.05714$	$\frac{4 \times 1075.213}{33,000} = 0.13033$	$\frac{4 \times 3848.460}{33,000} = 0.46648$
Crank-End (C')=$\frac{L \times A'}{33,000}$		$\frac{4 \times 432.951}{33,000} = 0.05248$	$\frac{4 \times 1036.728}{33,000} = 0.12566$	$\frac{4 \times 3809.975}{33,000} = 0.46182$

CALCULATION: Indicator Diagrams were taken with the propeller turning 64.6 rpm (N)

		HP	IP	LP
Head-End Area	Sq. In.	3.12	4.85	3.02
Crank-End Area	Sq. In.	3.22	4.70	3.12
Length (extreme)	In.	3.75	3.92	3.60
Spring Scale (S)	Psi.	125.00	40.00	16.00
$\frac{\text{Head-End Area}}{\text{Length}} = 0$		$\frac{3.12}{3.75} = 0.8320$	$\frac{4.85}{3.92} = 1.2372$	$\frac{3.02}{3.60} = 0.8389$
$\frac{\text{Crank-End Area}}{\text{Length}} = Q'$		$\frac{3.22}{3.75} = 0.8587$	$\frac{4.70}{3.92} = 1.1990$	$\frac{3.12}{3.60} = 0.8667$
$0 \times S = Pm$		$0.8320 \times 125 = 104.000$	$1.2372 \times 40 = 49.488$	$0.8389 \times 16 = 13.422$
$0' \times S = P'm$		$0.8587 \times 125 = 107.338$	$1.1990 \times 40 = 47.960$	$0.8667 \times 16 = 13.867$
$Pm \times C \times N = IHP$ Head-End		$104.000 \times 0.05714 \times 64.6 =$ 383.918	$49.488 \times 0.13033 \times 64.6 =$ 416.670	$13.422 \times 0.46648 \times 64.6 =$ 404.461
$P'm \times C' \times N = IHP$ Crank-End		$107.338 \times 0.05248 \times 64.6 =$ 363.892	$47.960 \times 0.12566 \times 64.6 =$ 389.344	$13.867 \times 0.46182 \times 64.6 =$ 413.698
		747.810	806.014	818.159
I H P		747.810	+ 806.014	+ 818.159 = 2371.983

APPENDIX D: NOTES ON FUEL CONSUMPTION

Fuel consumption at different speeds may be determined from data compiled during official vessel trials; such data is usually presented in the form of tables or graphs.

TABLE D-1

SPEED, FUEL CONSUMPTION, AND RANGE

	SPEED (Knots)	FUEL CONSUMPTION (bbls/day)			MEAN DRAFT	DEAD WEIGHT (Tons)	RANGE DAYS	NUMBER OF PASSAGES
		SEA	PORT					
			IDLE	CARGO				
LIBERTY EC2-S-C1	11.0	170			27'8-15/16"		72	
	10.0	150			"		81	
	9.0	130			"		94	
	8.0	110			"		111	
	6.5	80			"		153	
			20	35				
C-3 CARGO	18.0	428			28'6-7/8"		44	
	16.5	320			"		57	
	10.0	135			"		140	
	9.0	120			"		157	
	8.0	105			"		180	
	6.5	95			"		210	
			30	45				
MARINER CA-S-12	20.23	472			15'-19'	1875/4825		89
	20.24	499			19'-22'	4825/7125		34
	19.92	509			22'-28'	7125/11950		27
	19.79	545			28'-29'	11950/12775		13

MARINER – CA-S-12

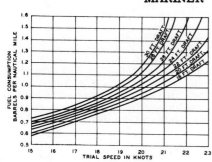

Fuel Consumption Versus
Speed-Trial Conditions

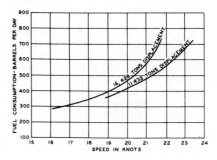

Fuel Rate Versus Speed Obtained
During Sea Trials, Corrected
To Standard Conditions

The above prototype trial and operational data has been extracted and pieced together from various easily accessible official and unofficial publications.

Generally, under conditions of fine weather, smooth water, and constant slip of the propeller, fuel consumption will vary roughly as the cube of the vessel's speed. When no other data is available, the following formula can provide a very rough, but often adequate guide:

$$\text{Amount of fuel per day at new speed} = \frac{(\text{New Speed in Knots})^3}{(\text{Old Speed in Knots})^3} \times \text{Amount of fuel per day at old speed}$$

A handy table showing consumption of fuel at sea for various speeds in different trades for a particular vessel or class of vessels can be useful to the owners or operators. Such a table may be expanded to fit one's needs and purposes; here is one variation:

TABLE D-2

FUEL CONSUMPTION AT DIFFERENT SPEEDS

Knots	Daily Fuel Consumption (Bbls)	Fuel Consumption at Sea (Bbls)		
		Trade A RVT-10 Days	Trade B RVT-15 Days	Trade C RVT-20 Days
17.00	Ballast 430	1720	2580	3440
	Loaded 500	2000	3000	4000
16.50	Ballast 393	1572	2358	3144
	Loaded 457	1828	2742	2656
16.00	Ballast 358	1432	2148	2864
	Loaded 417	1668	2502	3356
Add Constant for RVT Fuel Cons. (Bbls)		600	900	1200

Example: To find the round-voyage fuel consumption in Trade A for a vessel proceeding four days at 17 knots in ballast and four days at 16.50 knots loaded, we enter the table to arrive at 1720 bbls and 1828 bbls respectively. The constant of 600 bbls covers the two-day average amount of fuel consumed in ports, on bay and/or river and/or canal passages in Trade A, giving a total of 4148 bbls for the ten-day turnaround. In Trade B the respective breakdown is six ballast days, six loaded days, and three days for port time, canals, and approaches, giving a total of 6222 bbls for the fifteen-day turnaround.

APPENDIX E: NOTES ON CARGO ESTIMATES AND STANDARDS

Most countries are signatories to the 1930 International Load Line Convention. According to the regulations of this convention, it is not sufficient for a vessel merely to comply with the load-line regulations upon arrival at the port of discharge. If the vessel has to pass through sea areas which call for greater freeboard than in the port of loading, the cargo must be arranged so that the ship does not lie deeper in the water than is permitted when passing through this area. In many ports, authorities are very strict with regard to overloading. Verification can be easily accomplished by investigating additions to, and consumption of, fuel, water, stores, ballast and the cargo carried, proceeding backwards from arrival to all loading ports of call.

The Load Line Act of March 2, 1929, as amended, and the Coastwise Load Line Act of 1935, as amended, established a set of regulations. Applications of this law have been published by the United States Coast Guard,[1] which administers and enforces them.

Table E-1 traces an imaginary turnaround of a vessel proceeding in ballast from a United States East Coast port to the West Coast of South America to load a full cargo in bulk.

APPENDIX F: NOTES ON FUEL COEFFICIENTS

Among the fuel coefficients the following formula is considered the most reliable:

$$\frac{\text{Fuel}}{\text{Coefficient}} = \frac{\text{Displacement}^{2/3} \times \text{Speed}^3}{\text{Tons of Fuel per 24 Hours}}$$

This fuel coefficient is the same as the well known:

$$\frac{\text{Admiralty}}{\text{Coefficient}} = \frac{\text{Displacement}^{2/3} \times \text{Speed}^3}{\text{Horsepower}}$$

Both coefficients are based on the assumption that the resistance of a vessel is mainly frictional and therefore varies as the wetted surface which in turn is related to displacement to the two-thirds power; the resistance varies as the speed cubed. As these assumptions are not very sound except at low speeds, the coefficients must be used with discretion. Moreover, this method of comparison assumes similar ships running at about the same speed and under similar operating conditions as to management, routes, and quality of fuel.[2] Admiralty and fuel coefficients are said to plot very well against weather intensity or slip of the propeller.

Coefficients of this kind are good for internal use in a fleet, but not for comparing the efficiency of one ship with a competing vessel. The same restrictions apply to the various modifications of the fuel coefficient, such as:

$$\text{Formula A} = \frac{\text{Mean Displacement} \times \text{Full Speed Distance}}{\text{Total Fuel Consumed at Full Speed}}$$

$$\text{Formula B} = \frac{\text{Mean Displacement} \times \text{Total Distance}}{\text{Total Fuel Consumed for All Purposes at Sea}}$$

$$\text{Formula C} = \frac{\text{Mean Displacement} \times \text{Total Distance}}{\text{Total Fuel Consumed for All Purposes}}$$

---

[1] U.S. Coast Guard, *Load Line Regulations*, U.S. Government Printing Office, Washington, D.C., July 1, 1963, CG 176.

[2] C. C. Pounder, *Marine Diesel Engines*, 2nd Edition, George Newnes Limited, London, 1960, p. 662.

TABLE E-1
CARGO ESTIMATE CALCULATION

	Zone	Max. Draft	Deadweight	Tons/Inch
S/S Vessel --	Tropical	35' 0-3/8"	25,172 tons	87.68
	Summer	34' 3-7/8"	24,427 tons	87.53
	Winter	33' 7-3/8"	23,684 tons	87.25

GROSS TONS	USE COAST DEP	CONS	WCS AMERICA ARR	CONS	DEP	CONS	PAN CAN	CONS	LAT 20°N	CONS	LAT 36°N	CONS	USE COAST ARR
WATER	200	100	100	5	95	5	90	2	88	3	85	-	85
STORES	50	5	45	-	45	2	43	1	42	2	40	-	40
FUEL	1667	739	928	11	917	448	469	106	363	192	171	41	130
BALLAST	*	-	50	-	50	-	50	-	50	-	50	-	50
CARGO	-	-	-	-	**	-	-	-	-	-	-	-	**
MISC.	20	-	20	-	20	-	20	-	20	-	20	-	20
TOTAL	-	-	1143	16	1127	455	672	109	563	197	366	41	325

*As required   **See calculation below

a) APRIL 1 - JULY 15 - From Tropical to Summer Zone - (Lat 20°N)

34' 3-7/8" -	24427	tons	Summer draft & deadweight
+ 6-3/8" -	564		Vessel consumes to Lat. 20°N
34'10-2/8" -	24991		Allowed draft & deadweight-WCS America
	1127		Deductibles-WCS America
	23864		G.T. AVAILABLE FOR CARGO
- 6-3/8"	563		Deductibles at Lat. 20°N
34' 3-7/8" -	24427		Draft & deadweight at Lat. 20°N
- 2-6/8"	325		Deductibles-USE Coast
34' 1-1/8" -	24189		Draft & deadweight-USE Coast

b) JULY 16 - OCTOBER 31 - From Tropical to Summer Zone - (Panama Canal)

34' 3-7/8" -	24427	tons	Winter draft & deadweight
+ 5-2/8" -	455		Vessel consumes to Lat. 36°N
34' 9-1/8" -	24882		Allowed draft & deadweight-WCS America
	1127		Deductibles-WCS America
	23755		G.T. AVAILABLE FOR CARGO
- 5-2/8"	672		Deductibles at Panama Canal
34' 3-7/8" -	24427		Draft & deadweight at Panama Canal
- 4-0/0"	325		Deductibles-USE Coast
33' 11-7/8" -	24080		Draft & deadweight-USE Coast

c) NOVEMBER 1 - MARCH 31 - From Tropical to Summer (Lat. 20°N) then Winter (Lat. 36°N) Zone

33' 7-3/8" -	23684	tons	Winter draft & deadweight
+ 8-5/8" -	761		Vessel consumes to Lat. 36°N
34' 4-0/0" -	24445		Allowed draft & deadweight-WCS America
	1127		Deductibles-WCS America
	23318		G.T. AVAILABLE FOR CARGO
- 6-3/8"	563		Deductibles at Lat. 20°N
33' 9-5/8" -	23881		Draft & deadweight at Lat. 20°N
- 2-2/8"	366		Deductibles at Lat. 36°N
33' 7-3/8" -	23684		Draft & deadweight at Lat. 36°N
- 0-4/8"	325		Deductibles-USE Coast
33' 6-7/8" -	23643		Draft & deadweight-USE Coast

Example: With the following assumed average sea performance values:

Displacement   (Δ) — 15,000 tons
Speed   (V) — 16.00 knots
Fuel Consumption   — 30.00 tons/24 hours
Horsepower   — 7,000 BHP

the two principal coefficients would yield:

$$\frac{\text{Fuel}}{\text{Coefficient}} = \frac{\Delta^{\frac{2}{3}} \times V^3}{\text{Fuel Consumed}} = \frac{15,000^{\frac{2}{3}} \times 16^3}{30} = \underline{83,012}$$

$$\frac{\text{Admiralty}}{\text{Coefficient}} = \frac{\Delta^{\frac{2}{3}} \times V^3}{\text{BHP}} = \frac{15,000^{\frac{2}{3}} \times 16^3}{7,000} = \underline{356}$$

Note: Displacement (Δ) corresponding to a given mean draft may be determined from the deadweight and displacement scale shown on the ship's official capacity plans. Approximate displacement may be ascertained from the formula:

$$\text{Displacement } (\Delta) = \frac{\text{Length} \times \text{Breadth} \times \text{Draft}}{35} \times \frac{\text{Coefficient}}{\text{of Fineness}}$$

APPENDIX G: VISUAL CONTROL BOARDS AND DIAGRAMS

Scheduling and keeping a constant check on the day-to-day position of vessels are important functions in a steamship operation. Among the control tools that have been developed, a good visual control board is superior to the colored pins or flags on maps that one sees in many operating departments. The principal advantage and purpose of visual control boards is to provide an instant survey of current, past, and future happenings within a given span of time. While most boards may serve well in a number of situations, no one board is best for every situation. An excellent article on control boards appeared in the July 1963 issue of *Administrative Management* (see Bibliography).

The boards themselves can be either magnetic or non-magnetic; the former seem to offer the most flexibility, particularly when the boards must be changed frequently. Many types and variations of visual control boards have been placed on the market. The board illustrated reveals a rather interesting and attractive feature, namely, a rotating sleeve that may solve the problem of running out of space.

An important feature of control boards, especially in scheduling, is the movable *Today* line which runs vertically from top to bottom of the board. The boards may be arranged to cover a period of say, three months; one horizontal column for every vessel with the vertical columns representing days of the month. A variety of colored signals, insert cards, or magnets may be used to denote various aspects of the operation of a fleet of vessels. Keeping the boards up-to-date is easy because a change means only an adjustment of the signals, cards, or magnets. Various problems that may develop far in the future can be spotted and prevented immediately.

Certain operational aspects of running a vessel or a fleet of vessels lend themselves to the application of statistical methods. Keeping statistics, whether in textual, tabular, or graphic form, should be preceded by forming clear ideas

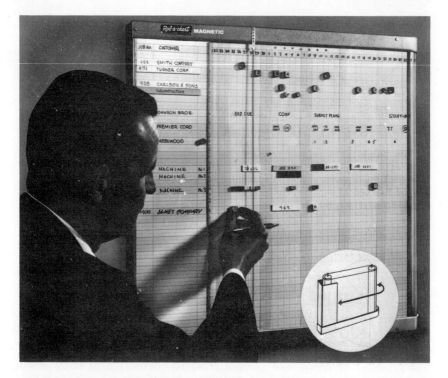

Rol-a-Chart magnetic visual control board (Wm. A. Steward Co.)

as to what is wanted. Tabular or graphic renderings are a matter of personal preference to some extent. Graphic presentation, however, should be used only if it can show numerical relationships more effectively than they can be shown with words or figures.

Among the various types of diagrams in use the following can be effective:

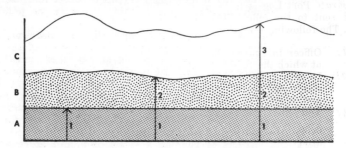

Band-Type Diagram

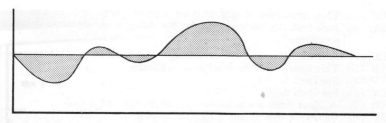

Silhouette-Type Diagram

This "high-low-average" type of diagram presents a continuous record of completed voyages by class and by trade. The ordinate axis may be graduated to show time in days, while the abscissa shows months or years. All the voyages can be marked along the vertical line connecting the low with the high, while the average voyage times are linked horizontally.

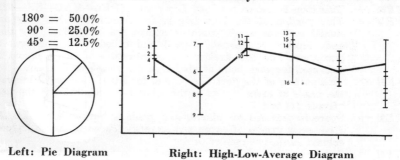

Left: Pie Diagram   **Right: High-Low-Average Diagram**

APPENDIX H: MISCELLANEOUS FORMS

ESSO INTERNATIONAL INC.
INSTRUCTIONS FOR COMPLETING PORT LOGS AND LOG ABSTRACTS

THE PORT LOG

A *separate* Port Log is to be prepared for *each* berth visited. The original is to be sent to the office. The twenty-four hour clock (0000-2400) should be used. The following remarks may be of assistance in preparing this form:

ITEM 1:   Officer in charge should obtain the correct name of the terminal at which the vessel is berthed.

ITEM 3:   In addition to the time, indicate the point where the sea passage was ended. It is generally the practice for vessel to take arrival and departure using local Standard Time.

ITEM 4:   You should report all operations in the order that they occur:

0000	5/ 2/66	—	0100	5/ 2/66	Proceeding to Pilot Station
0100	"	—	0200	"	Proceeding to Anchorage
0200	"	—	0800	"	Awaiting Tide
0800	"	—	0900	"	Proceeding to Dock
0900	"	—	0930	"	Docking

ITEM 4: This procedure should also be used in Items #7, 10 and 13. Be
(cont.) sure that the *basic* reason for the delay is shown when delays run
concurrently.

ITEM 10: Indicate *all* operations and delays. See Item 4.
ITEM 11: This item should be filled in if applicable.
ITEM 13: See Item 4.
ITEM 14: See Item 3.
ITEM 16: All four lines are to be used for lightering information.
ITEM 18: Officer in charge should obtain details of the shore facilities (i.e.,
size of lines and distance pumped, etc.) and shall request advice
on any changes made during discharge.
ITEM 22: This entry should show the *original* time posted on the sailing
board. If changes were made later, indicate the revised times and
the reasons for such changes under Item 29.

ITEM 23
and 24: Indicate the time tugs and pilots were ordered for undocking.
ITEM 25: This item is not on the Port Log form. (DEL—MAR—SH—429)
ITEM 26: This portion of the Port Log is for DISCHARGING only and
should indicate which pump or pumps are being used, the time
each product is started, stopped and ended. The pressures at
pump and rail, the strokes and temperature of cargo should be
indicated for *each* hour of discharge for *each* pump in use.

ITEM 27: This portion of the Port Log is used for LOADING only. Indicate
the grade of cargo loaded in the column directly beneath the item
"Grade (1) to (12)."

ITEM 28: Space is provided for ullages and grade of cargo. When LOAD-
ING, show grades of cargo and quantity loaded in the right-hand
column marked "Grade of Oil."

ITEM 29: This part of the form is to be used for remarks or if there is not
enough space under any particular other item. Fill in box marked
"Discharge Rates."

You will note that a space has been provided for the Chief Engineer to sign
all Port Log entries relating to the mechanical performance of the vessel or
its equipment.

THE LOG ABSTRACT

A separate Abstract of Deck and Engine Log (called "Abstract" for short-
ness) is to be prepared for every sea passage, or leg of each respective voyage,
and forwarded to this office.

The following is a guide in the preparation of the Abstract:

(a) All references to "In Port" time and consumption on each Abstract
pertain to the port of departure.

(b) Under these headings indicate consumption of *each* grade of fuel you
are using.

FUEL OIL AND FRESH WATER ACCOUNTS
FUEL CONSUMPTION—SEA PASSAGE
FUEL CONSUMPTION—PORT OF DEPARTURE

(c) DRAFT INFORMATION (on the reverse of the form). "Departure
from Dock" refers to the dock at the port of departure.

(d) DEADWEIGHT REPORT. Indicate allowed deadweight and draft
versus the actual total deadweight loaded (include calculated cargo,
bunkers, fresh water and stores). Compare the actual with the allowed deadweight and draft and give the reason for the difference.

PORT LOG

1. VESSEL		TERMINAL	FOR OFFICE USE ONLY LEAVE BLANK
2. PORT		BERTH	
3. ENDED SEA PASSAGE (SEE COMPANY REGULATIONS)		POINT USED	

4. OPERATIONS AND DELAYS – BETWEEN "ENDED SEA PASSAGE" AND "FAST TO PIER" (SHOW EACH ITEM SEPARATELY) | HOURS | HOURS |

FROM	UNTIL	CAUSE		

5. FAST TO PIER OR MOORING		TIME TENDERED		PASS. (IN)
6. 1ST HOSE CONNECTED AT	2ND	3RD	4TH	

7. OPERATIONS AND DELAYS – BETWEEN "FAST TO PIER" AND "STARTED LOADING OR DISHCARGING" (SHOW EACH ITEM SEP.)

FROM	UNTIL	CAUSE		

8. STARTED LOADING OR DISCHARGING		GIVE DETAILS OF PUMPING	
9. FINISHED LOADING OR DISCHARGING		ON PAGES TWO AND THREE	GROSS

10. OPERATIONS AND DELAYS – BETWEEN "FINISHED LOADING OR DISCHARGING" AND "CLEAR OF PIER" (SHOW EA. ITEM SEP.) | N.P. |

FROM	UNTIL	CAUSE		
				LTG.
				TOTAL N.P.

11. IF REQUIRED RATE NOT MAINTAINED STATE REASON	
12. ALL HOSE DISCONNECTED	CLEAR OF PIER

13. OPERATIONS AND DELAYS – BETWEEN "CLEAR OF PIER" AND "BEGAN SEA PASSAGE" (SHOW EACH ITEM SEPARATELY)

FROM	UNTIL	CAUSE		
				PASS.(OUT)
				TOTAL
				TOT. LESS RER & PASS.

14. BEGAN SEA PASSAGE (SEE COMPANY REGULATIONS)		POINT USED	NOM. D.W.T.
15. DRAFT (ARRIVING) FWD. AFT MEAN (SAILING) FWD. AFT. MEAN			SUPL.R. CONS.
16. IF CARGO LOADED FROM OR DISCHARGED INTO LIGHTERS FILL OUT FOLLOWING:			L. BEGIN

	1	2	3	4	
LIGHTER ALONGSIDE					L. END
START LOAD OR DISCH.					GROSS L.T. HR.
FINISH LOAD OR DISCH.					DEDUC'NS * HR.
LIGHTER LEFT					NET L.T. HR.

17. IF DELAYED BY REPAIRS STATE GENERAL NATURE – WHAT BOILERS CLEANED	ALLOWED HR.
	EX./SURPLUS HR.

18. SHORE LINES USED: NUMBER SIZE IN.: LGTH.	21. MAXIMUM OIL PRESSURE ALLOWED ON HOSE:
SHORE LINES USED: NUMBER SIZE IN.: LGTH.	22. POSTED SAILING TIME
19. HOSE USED NUMBER SIZE INCH	23. TIME TUGS ORDERED (SAILING)
HOSE USED NUMBER SIZE INCH	24. TIME PILOT ORDERED (SAILING)

20. FUELING STARTED		FOR OFFICE USE ONLY	R.R.	ANALYST	T.A.	DEM.
FUELING FINISHED						

Esso International Inc.

DISCHARGING

TIME EACH START & STOP	GRADE EA. START CAUSE EA. STOP	OIL PRESS AT PUMP	OIL PRESS. SHIPS RAIL	CYCLES RPM OR STROKES	OIL TEMP. DURING DISCH.	TIME EACH START & STOP	GRADE EA. START CAUSE EA. STOP	OIL PRESS AT PUMP	OIL PRESS. SHIPS RAIL	CYCLES RPM OR STROKES	OIL TEMP. DURING DISCH.	TIME EACH START & STOP	GRADE EA.START CAUSE EA.STOP	OIL PRESS. AT PUMP
			PUMP						PUMP					
DATE														

GR.(10)	CAUSE OF STOPS (GRADES 9 & 10)	TIME OF EACH START & STOP	GR.(9)	GR.(8)	TIME OF EACH START & STOP	CAUSE OF STOPS (GRADES 7 & 8)	GR.(7)	GR.(6)	TIME OF EA. EACH START START & STOP & STOP	CAUSE OF STOPS (GRADES 5 & 6)

LOADING

128

	PUMP				PUMP						PUMP			
OIL PRESS. SHIPS RAIL	CYCLES RPM OR STROKES	OIL TEMP. DURING DISCH.	TIME EACH START & STOP	GRADE EA. START CAUSE EA. STOP	OIL PRESS. AT PUMP	OIL PRESS. SHIPS RAIL	CYCLES RPM OR STROKES	OIL TEMP. DURING DISCH.	TIME EACH START & STOP	GRADE EA. START CAUSE EA. STOP	OIL PRESS AT PUMP	OIL PRESS. SHIPS RAIL	CYCLES RPM OR STROKES	OIL TEMP. DURING DISCH.

(blank ruled form rows)

DATE

LOADING

CAUSE OF STOPS (GRADES 5 & 6)	TIME OF EACH START & STOP GR. (5)	TIME OF EACH START & STOP GR. (4)	CAUSE OF STOPS (GRADES 3 & 4)	TIME OF EACH START & STOP GR. (3)	TIME OF EACH START & STOP GR. (2)	CAUSE OF STOPS (GRADES 1 & 2)	TIME OF EACH START & STOP GR. (1)

129

Esso International Inc.

ULLAGE REPORT
IMMEDIATELY AFTER LOADING OR BEFORE DISCHARGING

TANK	PORT			CENTER			STARBOARD			GRADE OF OIL STATE UNDER "GENERAL REMARKS" IF ANY CARGO SHIFTED DURING VOYAGE OR ANY INNAGES AFTER DISCHARGING.
	FEET	INCHES	TEMP. FAHR.	FEET	INCHES	TEMP. FAHR.	FEET	INCHES	TEMP. FAHR.	
1										
2										
3										
4										
5										
6										
7										
8										
9										
10										
11										

INSPECTOR AT PORT

29. GENERAL REMARKS:

	DISCHARGE RATE (S)		
	NET BBLS./HR. MAINTAINED	CARGO	
		GRADE	GROSS BBLS. (42)

THE ABOVE ENTRIES ARE CERTIFIED TO BE CORRECT   NOTED FOR MECHANICAL PERFORMANCE   EXAMINED AND APPROVED

CHIEF OFFICER _____ CHIEF ENGINEER _____ MASTER _____

NOTE: A COMPLETE AND ACCURATE ACCOUNT IS REQUIRED OF ALL TIME SPENT IN PORT: ACCORDINGLY WHEN FORM IS INADEQUATE, USE ITEM 29 OR APPEND REPORT: FILL OUT SEPARATE FORM FOR EACH PORT OR EACH BERTH WITHIN A PORT VISITED. PREPARE FORMS IN DUPLICATE: RETAIN ONE COPY ON BOARD: SEND OTHER PROMPTLY TO THE NEW YORK OFFICE ON ARRIVAL NEXT PORT.

ABSTRACT OF DECK AND ENGINE LOG — Esso International Inc.

S/S	FROM	PORT OF DEPARTURE	TO	DESTINATION	BEGINNING — END OF LAST SEA PASSAGE	ENDING — END OF PRESENT SEA PASSAGE	LOADED/BALLAST

VOYAGE OPERATING TIME

	MONTH	DAY(S)	HOURS	MINUTES
END OF LAST SEA PASSAGE				
(A) START OF PRESENT SEA PASSAGE				
TOTAL TIME IN PORT	X X X			
(B) END OF PRESENT SEA PASSAGE				
(C) TIME CORRECTION DUE TO CHANGE OF LONGITUDE				
(D) TOTAL RUNNING TIME AT SEA (B—A PLUS OR MINUS C)				
(E1) STOPS OR BREAKDOWNS AT SEA – DATE				
STOPS OR BREAKDOWNS AT SEA – DATE				
(E2) TOTAL STOPPAGES AT SEA				
(F1) NET RUNNING TIME (D—E2)				
(F2) NET RUNNING TIME IN HOURS				
(F3) NET RUNNING TIME IN MINUTES				

TOTAL TIME SINCE 1ST OF YEAR

	DAYS	HOURS	MINUTES
RUNNING TIME AT SEA – LOADED			
RUNNING TIME AT SEA – BALLAST			
RUNNING TIME IN PORT			
TIME STOPPED AT SEA			
TIME STOPPED IN PORT			
COMBINE TIME (TOTAL OF ABOVE)			
OBSERVE MILES COVERED IN PASSAGE – LOADED			
OBSERVE MILES COVERED IN PASSAGE – BALLAST			
ENGINE MILES COVERED IN PORT			

REVOLUTIONS

COUNTER AT START OF PRESENT SEA PASSAGE	
COUNTER AT END OF LAST SEA PASSAGE	
(G1) TOTAL REVOLUTIONS IN PORT	
COUNTER AT END OF PRESENT SEA PASSAGE	
(G2) TOTAL SEA PASSAGE REVOLUTIONS	
(H) REVOLUTIONS PER MINUTE (G2/F3)	

HOURS IN USE — HOURS X UNITS	STEAM ON DECK LINES	EVAPORATOR	HEAT TO QUARTERS	BUNKER HEATING COILS	MAIN CARGO PUMPS	STRIPPING PUMPS
AT SEA						
IN PORT						

VOYAGE DATA

(J) DISTANCE RUN BY OBSERVATION AT SEA	
(K) MILES PER HOUR BY OBSERVATION (J ÷ F2)	
TOTAL ENGINE MILES $\frac{G2 \times PITCH}{6080}$ (L) SEA PASSAGE	
(M) SLIP – L – J ÷ L	
(N) REVOLUTIONS PER OBSERVED MILE (G2 ÷ J)	
(P) TOTAL BARRELS FUEL CONSUMED ON SEA PASSAGE	
(R) BARRELS FUEL CONSUMED PER 24 HOUR DAY (P x 24 ÷ F2)	
TOTAL ENGINE MILES IN PORT $\frac{G1 \times PITCH}{6080}$	

FUEL CONSUMPTION, PORT OF DEPARTURE (BARRELS)

	TIME — DAYS	HOURS	MINUTES	FUEL
FROM SEABUOY TO DOCK ENTERING				
IN LOADING OR DISCHARGING CARGO – (EXCLUDING BALLAST)				
WHILE AT ANCHOR OR DOCK OTHER THAN ABOVE				
FROM DOCK TO SEABUOY LEAVING				
TOTAL PORT TIME AND FUEL CONSUMPTION				

FUEL CONSUMPTION SINCE 1ST OF YEAR

	BARRELS
TOTAL ON BOARD AND RECEIVED SINCE FIRST OF YEAR	
TOTAL CONSUMED AT SEA, LOADED	
TOTAL CONSUMED AT SEA, BALLAST	
TOTAL CONSUMED IN PORT	
TOTAL CONSUMED AT SEA AND IN PORT	
AVERAGE BARRELS FUEL OIL PER DAY, LOADED	
AVERAGE BARRELS FUEL OIL PER DAY, BALLAST	

AVERAGE CONSUMPTION PER DAY SINCE FIRST OF YEAR TO BE CALCULATED BY DIVIDING CONSUMPTION AT SEA LOADED OR BALLAST BY CORRESPONDING RUNNING TIME.

ENGINE DATA

NOZZLE COMBINATION OR H.P.	
HOURS IN USE	
DATE OF LAST DRYDOCKING	
DATE OF LAST BOILER WASHING	

A SEPARATE ABSTRACT, COMPLETELY FILLED IN ON BOTH SIDES OF SHEET, IS TO BE MADE FOR EVERY SEA PASSAGE, OR LEG, OF EACH RESPECTIVE VOYAGE. IT MUST BE FORWARDED TO THE OFFICE IMMEDIATELY UPON VESSEL'S ARRIVAL IN PORT. EACH ABSTRACT IS TO COVER PERIOD BEGINNING AT END OF PREVIOUS SEA PASSAGE AND TERMINATING AT END OF FOLLOWING SEA PASSAGE. START AND END OF SEA PASSAGE WILL ALWAYS BE THE POINT SPECIFIED IN MARINE REGULATIONS. ALL TIME ENTRIES SHOULD BE STANDARD ZONE TIME.

ABSTRACT OF DECK AND ENGINE LOG

Esso International Inc.

VOYAGE FUEL OIL, FRESH WATER AND LUBE OIL ACCOUNTS
(*VESSELS WITHOUT L.P. EVAPORATORS LEAVE BLANK)

	FUEL OIL (BARRELS)	FRESH WATER (TONS)			LUBRICATING OILS (U.S. GALLONS)		
	STANDARD BUNKERS	BOILER	WASH	DRINKING	ENGINE OILS	OTHER LUBES	
ON HAND AT END OF LAST SEA PASSAGE							
RECEIVED AT PORT OF DEPARTURE							
TOTAL ON HAND AND RECEIVED							
LESS TOTAL PORT CONSUMPTION							
ON HAND AT START OF SEA PASSAGE							
*TOTAL WATER MADE WITH L.P. EVAPORATOR							
*TOTAL WATER MADE AND ON HAND							
CONSUMED ON SEA PASSAGE							
ON HAND AT END OF SEA PASSAGE							
CONSUMED PER 24 HOUR DAY AT SEA							

FUEL OIL ON BOARD

2400 12/31 _____ BBLS.

FINISH LAST DISCH. EACH _____ BBLS.

MONTH, EST.

ACTUAL DRAFTS

	F FORWARD	A AFT.	MEAN (F+A / 2)	AMIDSHIPS	
				PORT	STARBOARD
DEPARTURE FROM DOCK					
START OF PASSAGE					
END OF PASSAGE					
ARRIVAL AT DOCK					

	(1) SPECIFIC GRAVITY OF WATER	(2) FREEBOARD ALLOWANCE (FUEL, ETC.) CONSUMED TO START OF SEA PASSAGE	FREEBOARD CORRECTION FOR (1) AND (2)
START OF PASSAGE			
END OF PASSAGE			

FUEL CHARACTERISTICS:
GRAVITY A.P.I.:
VISCOSITY:
FLASH:
REMARKS

BUNKERS			DEEP TANK
PORT	CENTER	STBD.	
FUEL (BARRELS)			
START OF PASSAGE			
END OF PASSAGE			

FRESH WATER (TONS)		
	START OF PASSAGE	END OF PASSAGE

ENGINE ROOM

AFT PEAK	FORE PEAK	DOMESTIC		DISTILLED
		BRIDGE	AFT	

TANK CLEANING

NO. MACH. IN USE	HOURS IN USE	AVG. PRES. AT PUMP	TEMP. WATER TO HEATER	TEMP. WATER FROM HEATER

CARGO HEATING

	NUMBER IN USE	HOURS IN USE	RETURNS
COILS			
CENTERS			
WINGS			

LIST TANKS CLEANED

WEATHER

WATER

AT SEA

STOPS

NAMES OF PILOTS

NAMES OF DOCKING MASTERS AND TUGS

MISCELLANEOUS AND/OR DIVERSION ORDERS**

MASTER

CHIEF ENGINEER

**IF VESSEL RECEIVES DIVERSION ORDERS, ALWAYS RECORD DATE, TIME AND POSITION EVEN THOUGH THERE IS NO ADDITIONAL STEAMING INVOLVED.

ABSTRACT OF DECK AND ENGINE LOG – STEAM AND MOTOR

Esso International Inc.

(TIME CHARTERED VESSELS)

/S _____

FROM _____ TO _____
(PORT OF DEPARTURE)   (DESTINATION)

LOADED/BALLAST PASSAGE
(DELETE IF NOT APPLICABLE)

BEGINNING _____ ENDING _____
(END OF LAST SEA PASSAGE)   (END OF PRESENT SEA PASSAGE)

OPERATING TIME

	MONTH	DAY (S)	HOUR	MINUTES
END OF LAST SEA PASSAGE				
(A) START OF PRESENT SEA PASSAGE				
TOTAL TIME IN PORT	XXX			
(B) END OF PRESENT SEA PASSAGE				
(C) TIME CORRECTION DUE TO CHANGE OF LONGITUDE				
(D) TOTAL RUNNING TIME AT SEA (B–A PLUS OR MINUS C)				
(E1) STOPS OR BREAKDOWNS AT SEA – DATE				
STOPS OR BREAKDOWNS AT SEA – DATE				
STOPS OR BREAKDOWNS AT SEA – DATE				
STOPS OR BREAKDOWNS AT SEA – DATE				
(E2) TOTAL STOPPAGES AT SEA				
(F1) NET RUNNING TIME (D–E2)				
(F2) NET RUNNING TIME IN HOURS				

FUEL OIL AND FRESH WATER ACCOUNTS

	FUEL OIL (BARRELS) (INSERT GRADES BELOW)	FRESH WATER (TONS)		
(**VESSELS WITHOUT L.P. EVAPORATORS LEAVE BLANK.)		BOILER	WASH	DRINKING
ON HAND AT END OF LAST SEA PASSAGE				
RECEIVED AT PORT OF DEPARTURE				
ON HAND AT START OF SEA PASSAGE				
*TOTAL WATER MADE WITH EVAPORATOR				
*TOTAL WATER MADE AND ON HAND				
CONSUMED ON SEA PASSAGE				
ON HAND AT END OF SEA PASSAGE				
CONSUMED PER 24 HOUR DAY AT SEA				

MASTER _____

CHIEF MATE _____

VOYAGE DATA

(G) DISTANCE RUN BY OBSERVATION AT SEA	
(H) MILES PER HOUR BY OBSERVATION ($\frac{G}{F2}$)	
(I) REVOLUTIONS PER MINUTE	

FUEL CONSUMPTION – SEA PASSAGE (BARRELS)
(INSERT GRADES BELOW)

(J) BY MAIN PROPULSION	
(K) BY BOILERS	
(L) BY AUXILIARIES	

FUEL CONSUMPTION – PORT OF DEPARTURE (BARRELS)

	TIME		MAIN PROPUL.	BOILERS	AUX.
	DAYS	HRS.	MINS.		(INSERT GRADES BELOW)
FROM SEABUOY TO DOCK ENTERING					
IN LOADING OR DISCHARGING CARGO (EXCLUDING BALLAST)					
WHILE AT DOCK OR ANCHORAGE OTHER THAN ABOVE					
FROM DOCK TO SEABUOY LEAVING					
TOTAL PORT TIME AND FUEL CONSUMPTION					

FUEL CHARACTERISTICS – (INSERT GRADES BELOW)

GRAVITY A.P.I. OF LAST DELIVERY	

CHIEF ENGINEER _____

A SEPARATE ABSTRACT, COMPLETELY FILLED IN ON BOTH SIDES OF SHEET, IS TO BE MADE FOR EOR EVERY SEA PASSAGE, OR LEG OF EACH RESPECTIVE VOYAGE. IT MUST BE FORWARDED TO THE OFFICE IMMEDIATELY UPON VESSEL'S ARRIVAL IN PORT. EACH ABSTRACT IS TO COVER PERIOD BEGINNING AT END OF PREVIOUS SEA PASSAGE AND TERMINATING AT END OF FOLLOWING SEA PASSAGE. ALL ENTRIES SHOULD BE STANDARD ZONE TIME.

ABSTRACT OF DECK AND ENGINE LOG – STEAM AND MOTOR   Esso International Inc.   PAGE 2

DRAFT INFORMATION

	ACTUAL DRAFTS				SPECIFIC GRAVITY OF WATER	INDI-CATED HOG OR SAG
	F FORWARD	A AFT	MEAN $\frac{F+A}{2}$	AMIDSHIPS PORT	AMIDSHIPS STBD.		
DEPARTURE FROM DOCK START OF PASSAGE (S/B)							

DEADWEIGHT REPORT FOR _____ LOADING PORT _____

ALLOWED DEADWEIGHT AND DRAFT
IN ACCORDANCE INTERNATIONAL
LOAD LINE REGULATIONS: DWT _____ *DRAFT _____

(A) _____   FT. _____ INS.

*INDICATE AS EQUIVALENT SALT WATER DRAFT

ACTUAL DEADWEIGHT LOADED

CARGO (SHORE FIGURES IF POSSIBLE) _____ TONS

BUNKERS _____

FRESH WATER _____

STORES _____

TOTAL DEADWEIGHT   (B) _____

DIFFERENCE (A–B) _____

REASON FOR DIFFERENCE BETWEEN (A) AND (B):–

REMARKS: (EXPLAIN FULLY, NOTATIONS MUST BE MADE ON ITEMS LISTED BELOW)

TANK CLEANING – (LIST TANKS CLEANED):

WEATHER:

STOPS AT SEA:

DATE OF LAST DRYDOCKING:

DATE OF LAST BOILER WASHING/ENGINE OVERHAUL:

NAMES OF PILOTS:

NAMES OF DOCKING MASTERS AND TUGS:

CARGO HEATING (INDICATE TIME HEAT ON CARGO):

MISCELLANEOUS:

134

ENGINE ABSTRACT LOG

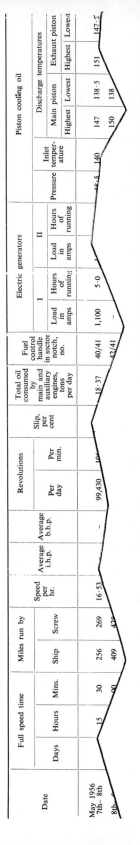

Date	Full speed time			Miles run by		Speed per hr.	Average i.h.p.	Average b.h.p.	Revolutions		Slip, per cent	Total oil consumed by main and auxiliary engines, tons per day	Fuel control handle in sector notch, no.	Electric generators I		Electric generators II		Pressure	Inlet temperature	Piston cooling oil — Discharge temperatures — Main piston		Exhaust piston	
	Days	Hours	Mins.	Ship	Screw				Per day	Per min.				Load in amps	Hours of running	Load in amps	Hours of running			Highest	Lowest	Highest	Lowest
May 1956 7th–8th		15	30	256	269	16·53	–		99,430	106		18·37	40/41	1,100	5·0	–		18·5	140	147	138·5	151	147·5
8th		60		409	428								42/41							150	138		

Pressure	Cylinder cooling water — Discharge temperatures — Highest	Lowest	Gas temperatures inlet turbine — Top — Highest	Lowest	For'd	Aft	Blower revolutions — For'd	Aft	Fuel injection pressure	Scavenge blowers air pressure	Filter — Before	After	Main engine lubricating oil cooler — Temperatures — Inlet	Outlet	Water Outlet	Main engine F.W. cooler temperatures — Sea — Outlet	Fresh water — Inlet	Outlet	Aux. engine lub. oil coolers — Oil outlet temperatures — No. 1	No. 2	Aux. engine F.W. cooler temperatures — Sea — Outlet	Fresh water — Inlet	Outlet	Sea temperature	Engine room temperature
37	160	148	780	730						3·9	29·5	27·5	110·5	103·5	90	140	160		115		82	136			80
		148								4·0	29	27			91	141									

Efficiency :: 129 per cent   Fuel per i.h.p. hr. :: 0·332 lb.
Efficiency :: 131·7 per cent   Fuel per b.h.p. hr. :: 0·384 lb.

Mechanical efficiency .. 86·5 per cent

Admiralty coefficient :: 412
Fuel coefficient .. :: 100,400

$$\text{Formula A} = \frac{\text{Mean displacement} \times \text{full steam distance}}{\text{Total fuel consumed at full speed}} = 209{,}571$$

$$\text{Formula B} = \frac{\text{Mean displacement} \times \text{total distance}}{\text{Total fuel consumed for all purposes at sea}} = 210{,}082$$

$$\text{Formula C} = \frac{\text{Mean displacement} \times \text{total distance}}{\text{Total fuel consumed for all purposes}} = 209{,}704$$

Esso International Inc. **PORT AGENT REPORT**

VESSEL		PORT	
DRAFT ON ARRIVAL: FORE	AFT	TERMINAL	
TIME OF ARRIVAL OFF SEABUOY (INBOUND)		BERTH	
TIME TENDERED		CONSIGNEE	
TIME ALL FAST TO PIER OR MOORING			
TIME FIRST HOSE CONNECTED	NO.	DIAMETER	INCHES

CAUSE OF EACH DELAY BETWEEN "ARRIVAL OFF SEABUOY" AND STARTING LOADING OR DISCHARGING

FROM	TO	CAUSE OF DELAY

BALLAST INFORMATION – LOADING PORT

		AV. DISCHARGE RATE – BBLS/HR.			
QUANTITY ON BOARD ON ARRIVAL AT DOCK	BBLS.	OVERBOARD	ASHORE	DIAMETER & LENGTH OF SHORE LINE	
NO. OF TANKS CONTAINING BALLAST				AVERAGE PRESSURE ON HOSE	

LOADING OR DISCHARGING PUMPING DATA

STARTED			STOPPED			CAUSE OF STOPPAGE
HOUR	DATE	WHICH PUMP	HOUR	DATE	WHICH PUMP	

AVERAGE NET LOADING OR DISCHARGING RATE MAINTAINED _____ BBLS. (42'S) PER HOUR

NUMBER, SIZE AND LENGTH OF SHORE LINES USED

DISCHARGING INFORMATION ONLY	WAS SHIP'S OR SHORE STEAM USED ?
	AVERAGE STEAM PRESSURE OR AMPS. AT SHIPS PUMPS
	MAX. OIL PRESSURE ALLOWED ON HOSE BY SHORE (DOCK GAUGE)
	AVERAGE OIL PRESSURE MAINTAINED ON HOSE (DOCK GAUGE)

IF REQUIRED DISCHARGING RATE NOT MAINTAINED STATE REASON

GRADE CARGO	QUANTITY IN BBLS. (42'S) AT 60°F.	AVG. TEMP. OF CARGO WHILE LOADING OR DISCH.

BUNKER FUEL: STARTED	FINISHED	QUANTITY
TIME CARGO HOSE DISCONNECTED	TIME ALL CLEAR OF PIER OR MOORING	

CAUSE OF DELAY BETWEEN FINISHING LOADING OR DISCHARGING & ARRIVAL AT SEABUOY (OUTBOUND)

FROM	TO	CAUSE OF DELAY

TIME OF DEPARTURE FROM SEABUOY (OUTBOUND) _____ DRAFT SAILING: FORE _____ AFT

SIGNED _____ (AGENT)

EXPLAIN ALL EXCEPTIONAL CIRCUMSTANCES ON REVERSE SIDE

PORT AGENT REPORT

OPERATION

☐ Loading
☐ Discharging

Vessel	Class	Voyage No.	Date
Port	Pier		Cargo No.

	DATE	TIME		DATE	TIME
FINISHED PASSAGE AT _____			PERMISSION GIVEN TO LOAD / discharge		
ARRIVED AT _____			SHIFTED TO LOADING / discharging berth		
PRATIQUE GIVEN			ALONGSIDE AND MOORED		
REPORTED TO CUSTOMS			BEGAN LOADING / discharging		
ENTERED AT CUSTOM HOUSE			FINISHED LOADING / discharging		
NOTICE OF READINESS DELIVERED			SAILED		

DETAIL OF TIME LOADING / DISCHARGING

DATES	STARTED AT: TIME	STOPPED AT: TIME	Act. Time Used Hrs.	Min.	Time Lost Hrs.	Min.	TONS	REMARKS SUNDAYS, HOLIDAYS, BAD WEATHER, ETC.

STOWAGE OF CARGO

HATCH NUMBERS										TOTALS
Location										
TONS										

TONNAGE AS PER BILL OF LADING

Outturn

(STATE IN FULL ANY CONDITIONS OR OTHER REASONS FOR UNUSUAL DELAYS IN LOADING CARGO.)

DRAFT OF VESSEL				WATER
	Fwd.	Aft	Mean	
Arrival				
Sailing				☐ Fresh ☐ Partly Fresh ☐ Salt

NOTE: Please cross out whatever does not apply.

APPROVED AND TIME CERTIFIED

_____ MASTER   SIGNED _____

137

VESSEL DISPATCH REPORT

Report No._____

/S _____ Voy. No. _____ Port _____

From: _____ Arrival D&T _____ Pilot Boarded _____

Sea Dist. _____ Miles   Time_____ d_____ h_____ m   Speed _____
          Time   Passage   Total
Pilot Dist. _____ F.W.E _____ Total Time _____ d_____ h _____ m   Dist. _____
                                                                          No.
Name/No. Berth/Anchorage/Position _____ Tugs _____
                                                   Per
Bbls. Fuel Consumed: Sea Passage_____ Knt._____ Det. _____

Delays On Passage/Detention Awaiting Berth/Reasons _____
_____
_____

Passengers: Arriving_____Debarked_____Embarked_____Sailing_____
Cargo: Tons Arriving_____Dischg'd_____Loaded_____Sailing_____
Mail Sacks: Arriving_____Dischg'd_____Loaded_____Sailing_____
Fuel Bbls: Arriving_____Consumed_____Rec'd_____Sailing_____
Water Tons: Arriving_____Consumed_____Rec'd_____Sailing_____
Draft: Arriving   F._____A._____M._____
Draft: Sailing   F._____A._____M._____

Left Berth Date/Time _____ Time In Port _____D_____H_____M   No. Tugs _____
Pilot Distance_____ Miles Departure Date/Time _____ For _____

Short General Remarks (Crew Changes, Cargo Operations, Shifts in Port, Weather in Port,
Accidents, Foreign Repairs, Detentions, Port Conditions, Etc.) Detailed Reports to be
Submitted Separately;

_____
_____
_____
_____
_____
_____
_____
_____
_____
_____

_____
                Master

Details of Cargo Operations see back of Sheet.

138

LOADING AND DISCHARGING TIMES

DATE	NO. GANGS	FORENOON FROM TO	AFTERNOON FROM TO	NIGHT FROM TO	REMARKS

Delay Fault of Vessel and Reasons _____

Delay Weather - Total Time and Reason _____

Delays Due Fault of Shippers and Receivers _____

Outturn of Cargo Remarks:

      Tally _____

      Shortage _____

      Overage _____

      Damage _____

Number of Exceptions taken on Mates Receipts _____

Distribution and Instructions:

To be Airmailed from the following Port

139

VOYAGE SUMMARY

/S _____

VOY. NO. _____

REPORT NO. _____

FROM _____ Date _____   TO _____ Date _____

PASSAGE REPORT

PORT FROM	PORT TO	BERTH TO BERTH DAY TIME DEP.	BERTH TO BERTH DAY TIME ARR.	TOTAL TIME STEAMING D H M	TOTAL DISTANCE	SEA DIST.	SEA SPEED	TOTAL DETEN-TIONS	FUEL BBLS USED	MILE
TOTALS										

PORT REPORT

PORT	PORT TIME D H M	FUEL USED	CARGO TONS DISCH.	CARGO TONS LOADED	MAIL SACKS DISCH	MAIL SACKS L'DED	PASSENGERS EMB.	PASSENGERS DEB.

TOTAL TIME ON VOYAGE _____

DISTRIBUTION:

MASTER _____
DATE _____

Bibliography

BOOKS

BAKER, GEORGE P., and GERMANE, GAYTON E., *Case Problems in Transportation Management*, McGraw-Hill Book Co., New York, 1957.

BES, J., *Tanker Shipping*, Uitgevereij VHC de Boer, Jr., Hilversum, Holland, 1963.

BONWICK, G. J., and STEER, E. C., *Ship's Business*, 4th ed., Maritime Press, London, 1961.

BOWNE, A. H. J., DOVE, C. A., and TOOTH, E. S., *Port Operation and Administration*, Chapman and Hall, Ltd., London, 1960.

BROSS, STEWARD R., *Ocean Shipping*, Cornell Maritime Press, Cambridge, Maryland, 1956.

COOLEY, HENRY B., *Freight Transportation for Profit*, Cornell Maritime Press, Cambridge, Maryland, 1946.

DOUGLASS, PAUL, *Communication Through Reports*, Prentice-Hall, Inc., Englewood Cliffs, N.J., 1957.

ELDEN, RODNEY M., *Ship Management: A Study in Definition and Management*, Cornell Maritime Press, Cambridge, 1962.

FERGUSON, ALLEN R., and others, *The Economic Value of the United States Merchant Marine*, The Transportation Center at Northwestern University, Evanston, Ill., 1961.

GRANT, EUGENE L., *Principles of Engineering Economy*, The Ronald Press, New York, 1950.

GREGORY, ROBERT, and VAN HORN, RICHARD, *Automatic Data Processing Systems*, Wadsworth Publishing Co., Belmont, Calif., 1964.

GROSSMAN, WILLIAM L., *Ocean Freight Rates*, Cornell Maritime Press, Cambridge, 1956.

HAY, WILLIAM W., *Introduction to Transportation Economics*, John Wiley & Sons, Inc., New York, 1961.

KEMP, J. F., and YOUNG, PETER, *Business for Shipmasters*, Kandy Publications, Ltd., Kenley, England, 1963.

LA DAGE, JOHN H., *Modern Ships: Elements of Their Design, Construction, and Operation*, Cornell Maritime Press, Cambridge, 1959.

LEBEDEV, E. P., *Transportnaya Statistika* (Transport Statistics), State Statistical Publishing House, Moscow, 1953.

MCCLOSKEY, JOSEPH F., and COPPINGER, JOHN M., editors, *Operations Research for Management*, Johns Hopkins Press, Baltimore, 1956.

MCDOWELL, CARL E., and GIBBS, HELEN M., *Ocean Transportation*, McGraw-Hill Book Co., New York, 1954.

MCFARLAND, MYRON, *Ship's Business and Cargo Loss and Damage*, Cornell Maritime Press, Cambridge, 1963.

METCALFE, JAMES V., *Principles of Ocean Transportation*, Simmons-Boardman Publishing Corp., New York, 1959.

NEWMAN, W. H., and SUMNER, JR., C. E., *The Process of Management*, Prentice-Hall, Inc., Englewood Cliffs, N.J., 1961.

NORTON, HUGH S., *Modern Transportation Economics*, Chas. E. Merrill Books, Inc., Columbus, Ohio, 1963.

PACE, HOMER ST. CLAIR, *Management and Costs*, Plandome Press, Inc., New York, 1934.

PLOWMAN, E. GROSVENOR, *Elements of Business Logistics*, Graduate School of Business, Stanford University, California, 1964.

POUNDER, C. C., *Marine Diesel Engines*, 2nd edition, George Newnes, Ltd., London, 1960.

REESE, HOWARD C., editor, *Merchant Marine Policy*, Cornell Maritime Press, Cambridge, 1956.

SCHMIDT, RICHARD N., and MEYERS, WILLIAM E., *Electronic Business Data Processing*, Rinehart, Winston, Holt, New York, 1963.

SEVERNS, WILLIAM H., and DEGLER, HOWARD E., *Steam, Air, and Gas Power*, 4th edition, John Wiley & Sons, Inc., New York, 1948.

STILIAN, GABRIEL N., and others, *PERT: A New Management Planning and Control Technique*, American Management Association, New York, 1963.

SVENDSEN, A. S., *Sea Transport and Shipping Economics*, Institute for Shipping Research, Bremen, 1958.

THEEL, GUSTAV ADOLPH, editor, *The World Shipping Scene*, Institute for Shipping Research, Munich, 1963.

WISSMAN, RUDOLPH WALTER, *The Maritime Industry*, Cornell Maritime Press, Cambridge, 1942.

TRANSACTIONS

AERTSSEN, G., "Sea Trials on a Victory Ship AP-3 in Normal Merchant Service," *Trans.*, 1953, Institution of Naval Architects (INA), London, vol. 95.

ALLAN, J. F., and CANHAM, H. J. S., "Ship Trial Performance and the Model Prediction," *Trans.*, 1954, INA, vol. 96.

ALLEN, W. G., and SULLIVAN, KEMPER, "Operation in Service of the Mariner-Type Ship," *Trans.*, 1954, Society of Naval Architects and Marine Engineers (SNAME), New York, vol. 62.

ATKINS, DONALD A., and HARBAUGH, ALLAN W., "Merchant Ship Maintenance and Reliability," SNAME, Southern California Section, Long Beach, February 11, 1965.

BENFORD, HARRY, "Engineering Economy in Tanker Design," *Trans.*, 1957, SNAME, vol. 65.

BONEBAKKER, IR. J. W., "The Application of Statistical Methods to the Analysis of Service Performance Data," *Trans.*, 1951, North East Coast Institution of Engineers and Shipbuilders (NECI), Newcastle-upon-Tyne, vol. 67.

—— "Analysis of Model Experiments, Trial, and Service Performance Data of a Single-Screw Tanker," *Trans.*, 1954, NECI, vol. 70.

BROWN, T. W. F., "The Measurement of Power," *Trans.*, 1955, INA, vol. 97.

BURRIL, L. C., "The Analysis of Trial Trip and Voyage Data," *Trans.*, 1956, Union Belge des Ingenieurs Navals, Brussels, vol. 4.

—— "Propellers in Action Behind a Ship," *Trans.*, 1960 Symposium, NECI, vol. 76.

CANHAM, H. J. S., CARTWRIGHT, D. E., GOODRICH, G. J., and HOGBEN, N., "Seakeeping Trials on O.W.S. *Weather Reporter*," *Trans.*, 1962, RINA, vol. 104.

CLEMENTS, R. E., "A Method of Analyzing Voyage Data," *Trans.*, 1957, NECI, vol. 73.

COOK, R., "Marine Torsionmeters and Thrustmeters," *Trans.*, 1951, Institute of Marine Engineers, London, vol. 63.

COUCH, R. B., and ST. DENIS, M., "Comparison of Power Performance of Ten 600-Foot Single-Screw Tanker Hulls as Predicted from Model Tests," *Trans.*, 1948, SNAME, vol. 56.

DATZ, I. M., and others, "A Description of the Maritime Administration Mathematical Simulation of Ship Operations," SNAME Annual Meeting, November 12, 1964, New York.

DIEUDONNE, J., and JOURDAIN, M., "Performance in Service of Cargo Vessel and Passenger Ships," *Trans.*, 1960 Symposium, NECI, vol. 76.

HANSON, ALVIN T., "The Cargo Vessel as a Materials Handling Unit," SNAME, Hawaii Section, September 17, 1957.

HUGHES, G., "Correlation of Model Resistance and Application to Ship," *Trans.*, 1963, RINA, vol. 105.

LEWIS, E. V., "Research Toward More Efficient Transportation by Sea," *Trans.*, 1961, SNAME, vol. 69.

LOGAN, A., "Service Performance of a Fleet of Tankers," *Trans.*, 1960 Symposium, NECI, vol. 76.

MACCUTCHEON, E. M., "Maritime Administration Research and Development," SNAME, Annual Meeting, November 14, 1963, New York.

MÖCKEL, W., "Fahrtnerlust der Schiffe in Seegang aus Fahrstbesbathtungen" (The Loss of Speed in Ships in a Seaway as Determined by Voyage Observations), *Schiff u. Werft*, 1944, vol. 25.

MOOR, D. I., "A Method of Predicting Measured Mile Performance from Tank and Trial Results," *Trans.*, 1960 Symposium, NECI, vol. 76.

MORREL, ROBERT C., "The Sea Speed of Modern Tankers," SNAME, New York Metropolitan Section Meeting, September 22, 1964.

MUNTON, RUPERT, "Some Shipowners' Problems," *Trans.*, 1959, NECI, vol. 75.

NEWMAN, RAYMOND, "The Relationship between Ships and Terminals," SNAME, New York Metropolitan Section Meeting, March 25, 1965.

SHEPHEARD, VICTOR G., "The Prediction of Ship Performance from Model Tests: The Nature of the Problem," *Trans.*, 1960 Symposium, NECI, vol. 76.

SMITH, S. L., "B.S.R.A. Resistance Experiments on the *Lucy Ashton*," *Trans.*, 1955, RINA, Part IV, vol. 97.

—— and CLEMENTS, R. E., "Service Performance Trials Carried Out in the North Atlantic on s/s *Cairndhu*," *Trans.*, 1958, NECI, vol. 74.

TAYLOR, J. LOCKWOOD, "Statistical Analysis of Voyage Abstracts," *Trans.*, 1928, RINA, vol. 70.

TELFER, E. V., "The Reconciliation of Model Data, Measured Mile Results and Service Performance of Ships," *Trans.*, 1960 Symposium, NECI, vol. 76.

—— "The Practical Analysis of Merchant Ship Trials and Service Performance," *Trans.*, 1926/27, NECI, vol. 43.

—— "Merchant Ship Service Performance Analysis," *Trans.*, 1929, Institute of Marine Engineers, vol. 41.

THWAITES, R. M., "The Economics of Ship Time," *Trans.*, 1959, NECI, vol. 75.

REPORTS

BENFORD, HARRY, *Some Observations on Immediate Goals for Maritime Research*, American Merchant Marine Conference, The Propeller Club of the United States, October 12, 1961.

BONEBAKKER, IR. J. W., *On Collecting Ship Performance Data and Their Analysis*, Report T.N.D., No. 10S, 1953.

BRARD, R., and JOURDAIN, M., *A New Method for Analyzing the Results of Sea Trials*, CBRN (Centre Belge de Recherches Navales) Congress, Brussels, 1963.

BRITISH SHIPBUILDING RESEARCH ASSOCIATION (BSRA), *Code of Procedure for Measured Mile Trials*, Report No. 145, 1954.

Code on Maneuvering and Special Trials and Tests, SNAME, Bulletin, 1950.

DANISH SHIP RESEARCH INSTITUTE, *Ship Trial Trip Code*, Copenhagen, 1964.

FARMER, RICHARD N., *Technical Studies in Transportation: Transportation Cost Finding*, Report No. 63-65, Department of Engineering, University of California, Los Angeles, December 1963.

FRIEDMAN, CARL A., *A Computer Simulation of the Matson Navigation Company's Freight-Fleet Operations*, 2 volumes, Report No. TO-B59-7, Technical Operations, Inc., April 1959.

HOGBEN, N., "Sea State Observation Studies on the s.s. *Cairndhu* and r.v. *Ernest Holt*," National Physical Laboratory, Ship Division Report No. 32.

——— "A Study of Voluntary Observer Ship Data for the North Atlantic," National Physical Laboratory, Ship Division Report No. 33.

MARITIME FOOD CONSULTANTS and PORT STEWARDS ASSOCIATION, *Subsistence Stores Record Book*, Graham-Chrisholm, Inc., New York.

NATIONAL ACADEMY OF SCIENCES-NATIONAL RESEARCH COUNCIL, Maritime Research Advisory Committee, *Proposed Program for Maritime Administration Research*, 2 volumes, 1960.

NATIONAL ACADEMY OF SCIENCES-NATIONAL RESEARCH COUNCIL, *U.S. Transportation: Resources, Performance, and Problems*, Publication 841-S, 1961.

NATIONAL SHIPPING AUTHORITY, Maritime Subsidy Board, *Index of Current Regulations of the Maritime Administration*, Govt. Printing Off., Washington, D.C., revised 1964.

ORGANIZATION OF AMERICAN STATES (OAS), *Second Inter-American Port and Harbor Conference*, Doc. 75, June 12, 1963.

Standardization Trials Code, SNAME, Bulletin, 1949.

TRANSPORTATION ASSOCIATION OF AMERICA, *Transportation Research*, Chicago, Ill., 1965.

UNITED AIRCRAFT CORPORATION, Norden Division, *Merchant Ship Automation Study*, report to U.S. Maritime Administration, June 1961.

U.S. COAST GUARD, *Load Line Regulations*, Govt. Printing Off., Washington, July 1, 1963, CG 176.

U.S. CONGRESS, House, Committee on Merchant Marine and Fish-
eries, *Study of the Operations of the Maritime Administration
and the Federal Maritime Board*, Hearings . . . February 2-25,
1955, 84th Cong., 1st Session, Govt. Printing Off., Washington.
U.S. DEPARTMENT OF COMMERCE, U.S. Maritime Administration,
Maritime Subsidy Policy, Washington, D.C., 1954.
U.S. LAWS, STATUTES, etc., *The Merchant Marine Act of 1936 As
Amended to 1956*, Govt. Printing Off., Washington, 1957.

ARTICLES AND PAPERS

BAKER, G. S., "Ship Efficiency and Economy," *The Journal of Com-
merce and Shipping Telegraph*, Liverpool, 1946.
BAMBERGER, WERNER, "Economy Sought in Ship Subsidies," *The
New York Times*, March 2, 1965.
BENJAMIN, ALAN, "The Total Systems Approach in Shipowning
Management," *Fairplay Shipping Journal*, London, January
9, 1964.
———— "Controlling the Liner Company of the Future," *Fairplay
Shipping Journal*, London, January 14, 1965.
BRUCE, HARRY J., and ZIONTS, STANLEY, "Research: The Forgotten
R in Transportation," *Transportation Journal*, Chicago, Sum-
mer, 1963, American Society of Traffic and Transportation,
vol. 2.
CALLAHAN, JOHN P., "Oil Fleet Acting to Cut Port Time," *The
New York Times*, February 21, 1965.
"Control Boards from Pegs to PERT," *Administrative Manage-
ment*, New York, vol. XXIV, No. 7, July 1963.
COOLEY, HENRY B., "Water Transportation Operation Analysis,"
Marine News, New York, October 1946.
DANIELS, W., "Operational Research into Shipping," *Fairplay
Shipping Journal*, London, January 14, 1965.
DENHOLM, J. F., *The Problem of Time in Shipping Economics*,
presented to the Institution of Engineers and Shipbuilders,
Glasgow, March 2, 1965.
"Designing New Vessels for an Old Trade," *Fairplay Shipping
Journal*, London, January 14, 1965.
DOUST, D. J., "A Statistical Model of Ship Performance in Service
Conditions," presented to joint meeting of the Institute of
Marine Engineers and the Royal Institution of Naval Archi-
tects, London, February 22, 1966.
DUGGAN, R. M., and FIELD, R. S., "A Statistical Approach to Ship
Performance," presented to joint meeting of the Institute of
Marine Engineers and the Royal Institution of Naval Archi-
tects, London, February 22, 1966.

EWART, W. D., "Control Engineering: a Factor in Marine Machinery Design," Europort Congress, Rotterdam, 1964.

"First Year's Service of the *Demodocus*," *The British Motor Ship*, London, October 1956.

FRENCH, WENDELL, "Process vis-à-vis Systems: Toward the Model of the Enterprise and Administration," *Journal of the Academy of Management*, Bloomington, Indiana, vol. VI, No. 1, March 1963.

GARRISON, JOEL, "The Systems Engineering Approach to Cargo Handling," *ICHCA Journal*, London, No. 7, July 1964.

GEORGIADES, J. C., "The Application of Computers to the Shipping Industry," *ICHCA Journal*, London, No. 8, October 1964.

GILL, WILLIAM A., "Survey Principles and Techniques," *Modern Management*, Washington, D.C., Jan.-Nov. 1949.

HINDS, G. H., "Electronics in Transport," *The Journal of the Institute of Transport*, vol. 28, No. 11, July 1960.

HOLUBOWICZ, R. P., and others, "Port of the Future," *Progress in Cargo Handling*, International Cargo Handling Coordination Association (ICHCA), Cornell Maritime Press, Inc., Cambridge, Md., vol. 3, 1962.

KAUDERN, G., *Some Aspects of Automation in Ships*, presented to the Royal Institution of Naval Architects, Gothenburg, September 7, 1961.

KENDALL, LANE C., "Experience and Judgment are Basic for Good Steamship Schedule," *Marine Engineering/Log*, New York, April 1956.

LEHMAN, G., "Neue Statistische Methoden zur Auswertung der Reiseergebnisse von Seeschiffen" (New Statistical Methods for Evaluation of Service Results), *Schiffbau*, Bremen, vol. 39, 1938.

LEWIS, E. V., "Log Analyses," *Proceedings of Second Summer Seminar on Ship Behavior at Sea*, Stevens Institute of Technology, Hoboken, N.J., June 1958.

MATOSSIAN, B. G., "Value Analysis as an Industrial Technique," presented to the Institution of Engineers and Shipbuilders, Glasgow, March 16, 1965.

MCKENNA, D., "Work Study in Transport," *The Journal of the Institute of Transport*, London, vol. 28, No. 3, March 1959.

MEYER, JOHN R., "The Evaluation of Statistical Costing Techniques as Applied in the Transportation Industry," *American Economic Review*, Stanford, Calif., vol. LI, No. 2, May 1961.

MORISON, ROBERT T., "Search for Ship Automation Solution Starts," *The Journal of Commerce*, New York, December 20, 1963.

"Operations Research in Action," *Fairplay Shipping Journal*, London, January 14, 1965.

PERRY, JR., WILLIAM E., "There Is Profit in Those Forms," *Administrative Management*, New York, vol. XXIV, No. 2, Feb. 1963.

SCHMIDT, RICHARD N., "Management and the Electronic Computer," *Journal of the Academy of Management*, Bloomington, Indiana, vol. III, No. 3, December 1960.

SCOTT, J., and VICKERSTAFF, H., *Planned Maintenance for Steam Tankers*, presented to the Institute of Marine Engineers, London, January 22, 1963.

"Shell Tankers Experiment with Telemetry," *The Shipping World*, London, March 5, 1964.

SINCLAIR, G. F., "Engineering in Transport," *The Journal of the Institute of Transport*, London, vol. 28, No. 44, May 1959.

STURMEY, S. G., "What of that New Spirit among Owners?" *The Journal of Commerce 1964 Annual Review*, London, January 1965.

SVIKIS, EDGAR, "Some Operating Conditions Affecting the Design of Merchant Ships," *Marine News*, New York, August 1948.

TASSERON, K., "Some Remarks on the Slip and the Efficiency of Ship's Propellers," *Shipbuilding and Shipping Record*, London, March 5, 1959.

WELDON, FOSTER L., "Research in Steamship Operations," *Progress in Cargo Handling*, International Cargo Handling Coordination Association, Fairplay Publications, Ltd., London, vol. 4, 1964.

WILLMOTT, G. M. R., "Operational Research in Shipping," *Fairplay Shipping Journal*, London, April 8, 1965.

WILSE, TH., "Some Comments on Merchant Ship Trials," presented to the Institute of Marine Engineers, London, March 10, 1965.

THESES

HAYEN, EDWARD GEORGE, "Analysis of Steamship Accounting Procedures to Evaluate Present Use and Application of Standard Cost Principles," unpublished Master's thesis, Bernard M. Baruch School of Business and Public Administration, CCNY, June 1957.

RIDGEVILLE, JACK, "Cost Accounting for Operation of Ocean-Going Vessels; a Study of Cost Finding Procedures in Commercial Service," unpublished Master's thesis, Bernard M. Baruch School of Business and Public Administration, June 1951.

SAWYER, MYRON R., "A Study of the Economic Life of a Ship," unpublished Master's thesis, Massachusetts Institute of Technology, September 1960.